THE LAST MILLER

The Cornmills of Ayrshire

By James Pearson Wilson F.S.A. (Scot)

Compiled by

Agnes M.Wilson
Susan W. Smith B.Sc.

Published by
Ayrshire Archaeological and Natural History Society

Printed by
Walker & Connell Ltd, Hastings Square, Darvel, Ayrshire

Front cover illustration: Millmannoch Mill, c1910

ISBN 0-9527445-6-2

James Pearson Wilson F.S.A. (Scot)
leading the Glenfield Ramblers Association
on a walk around Fail and Tarbolton
in 1947.

CONTENTS

INTRODUCTION

James Pearson Wilson F.S.A. (Scot) (1872-1954) "The Miller", a noted antiquarian and Burnsian, was born at Faile Mill, Tarbolton. A miller himself, he came from a long line of millers and was one of the best known in Ayrshire.

His apprenticeship was served at Cunninghamhead, Almont Mill - Pinwherry, and at Kilmaurs. Following his marriage to Mary Elizabeth Donald, daughter of the miller at Irvinehill, he took over Milton Mill at Stair. After the birth of his first child he moved to Millmannoch Mill, the scene of Burns' song *The Soldiers Return,* and then to Privick Mill, Annbank.

He had a genius for research and a flair for discovering important historical matter in old records, and prints. His research work on Faile Monastery and Faile Castle gained his election to the Society of Antiquaries of Scotland, and The Ayrshire Archaeological Society published booklets on both of these subjects.

As a member of Tarbolton Literary Society he led a team compiling data for the making of the historical, geographical and geological record of Tarbolton parish and neighbouring Barnweil, known as the *Lorimer Map.* A project which took seven years to achieve, with much of the information and documents rescued personally from the destructor in Ayr. The map is still in ownership of the Lorimer Trust and can be seen in the Lorimer Library, Tarbolton.

He made a study of mills and milling in Scotland in the past, checking charters and sasines. Records were verified for all the mills he wrote about, and all the sites visited, speaking to the owner when possible and local residents He wrote several articles on many of the mills of Ayrshire, most of which were published in the Ayrshire Post between 1944 and 1948. He knew the sites and stories of old mills which had disappeared centuries ago. The contents of the articles are invaluable as a source of local milling and social history, derived from a mixture of technical detail, local tales and many other snippets of information he could acquire.

As miller of Milmannoch Mill at the time the famous Trysting Thorn died, he had it cut up, sending the pieces to the Mauchline Box Company for preservation in the form of mallets and plaques and printed with the verse from *The Soldiers Return* by Burns:

> *At last I reached the bonnie glen,*
> *where early life I sported,*
> *I passed the mill and trysting thorn,*
> *where Nancy aft I courted.*

Pieces of the trysting thorn in this state have been gifted to Burns Clubs all over the world. He was prime mover in having the old Bachelors' Club building restored and was honorary president of the committee elected to look after its affairs. He was also an ex-president and an honorary president of Burns's own debating club.

Although he had five sons and a daughter, it has been left to his grandchildren and great grandchildren to ensure that this legacy of information on the mills is made available to students of local history.

THE POW BURN[1]

With the attempt on the part of the Scottish Office to encourage the use of Scotland's food products in the rearing of a healthy nation during the Second World War, it was noted with some regret that many mills which made the foundation for the old standard food - oatmeal - were quickly disappearing. They had served their purpose maybe and yet were mills not still required to maintain the quantity and quality of the product ?

Historically mills were built in olden times on now mostly ruined sites to meet the requirements of the farmers. At their request, a landowner, who had water power on his land, was approached and guarantees given that, if he erected a mill, the adjacent landowners, who had not this power at hand, would bind their tenants to mill all their corn, with the exception of seed or horse corn, at this specific mill. This arrangement was called *thirlage*. The fee for grinding was called *multures* and was paid in meal, not in cash, but the amount varied according to a fixed agreement. This system continued for many hundreds of years until 1799, when an Act was passed to enforce the commutation of thirlage[2] and multures[3] to money payments. Full benefit of the Act was not taken by the farmers, and with the loss of the multures, many of the small mills were closed and fell into decay.

Many mills were to be found on the rivers of Ayrshire at one time but by 1944 the number had dwindled considerably. This is evidenced on the Pow Burn where at one time there were four mills operating, but by the time of writing not one was to be found. The small tributary of the Pow Burn from Barnweil Loch had also lost the Heugh Mill.

Near the mouth of the Pow Burn was Prestwick Mill, later called Monkton Mill. Not far away was Powbank, situated near Monkton. Further along was Adamton Mill and, at a point three quarters of a mile east of Symington was Helenton Mill, which also stood on the Pow Burn.

HELENTON MILL

This mill was driven by water from two dams, the nearest being at the Motehill - which may have been the court place of the barony as there was a ruin on the top - and the other was about two hundred yards further up the burn, equidistant from the mote and Damhead Farm. The mill was driven by a breast wheel with a fall of from ten to twelve feet. It was equipped with two pairs of what were reckoned to be the best Scottish mill stones which were quarried at Kameshill, West Kilbride. The oatmeal sieve was the commonly used three sheets - Nos. 9, 10 and 11 - and the mill was capable of milling half a ton of oatmeal per hour.

In addition to the making of oatmeal this mill produced provender for cattle. The owner was Montgomerie of Eglinton. When the mill closed in 1858 one half of the machinery belonged to the tenant and the other half to the proprietor. The miller bought the proprietor's half and removed it with his own on closure. The mill is of special interest to the writer as the last miller was his grandfather. It is also worthy of note that this was one of the mills erected by proprietors for the benefit of their tenants and was one of several which had joint owners. *William Wallace of Ellerslie had sasine of the XXX shilling land or thereby of Mains of*

Helenton and Bogend with the tour fortalise and manor thereof with the half of the mill of Helenton - dated 3rd March 1583.
This was a mill conveniently placed and maintained by the proprietors of two small estates to ensure that their tenants had a milling facility. Another case was stated by W Douglas Simpson: *By charter of Robert II, dated 18th October, 1372, confirming as assedation by Ingeram McGillilan (McLean) to Sir Robert Stewart of the whole davoch of the lands of Castleton, Hogstone and Westerbalblayne and the quarter of Morhouse in the barony of Redcastle above Lunan.* Yet another was: *John Mitchell of Turnerhill, who, in 1688, married Margaret, daughter of John Reid of Ballochmyle, had sasine of the £4 5/- land of Daldilling and half of the mill of Catrine - dated 12th June, 1699.*

HEUGH MILL

About a mile east of Helenton near to Underhill of Barnweil was Heugh Mill on the burn from Barnweil Loch or dam. The mill was built near a fall in the burn which made it a very suitable place for the water power. Like all the mills before the middle of the eighteenth century, this mill was driven by *cog and rung*. The cogwheel was fixed to the axle of the water wheel and the rung wheel to the spindle of the over millstone and meshed into each other sufficient in size to drive the stone at about one hundred and twenty revolutions a minute. Each pair of stones required a separate water wheel until the invention of cast-iron gears, which are said to be the work of the father and grandfather of William Murdock the pioneer of gas lighting. The rungs of the cog and rung were the most vital part of the mill and, consequently, a supply was always kept at hand to renew them when worn out or broken. Reference to the rungs was made by Burns in *To a Haggis*.
Your pin wad help to mend a mill
in time o' need.
James Mackie was the tenant of the mill in the middle of the nineteenth century. In this mill were found some old, perforated skin hand-sieves for sifting oatmeal and mashlam (mixed grain). These had been carefully preserved and kept in order and had been in use before the power driven sieves were introduced into the mills. Heugh Mill was finally closed about the year 1858.
The undernoted were millers on the Pow Burn in the middle of the nineteenth century: Adamton Mill - Alexander Calderwood; Powbank Mill - Hugh Ronald; Monkton Mill - Thomas Reid, farmer; Helenton Mill - John Wilson; Heugh Mill - James Mackie.

THE WATER OF FAIL [4]

Another river which had lost its mills by the 1940's was the Water of Fail. Near the junction with the River Ayr stood Failford Mill on the Yonderton Burn, and up the river past Coilsfield was Park Mill. At the outskirts of Tarbolton was Tarbolton Mill, the *Willie's Mill* of Burns poem. About a mile further up was Fail Mill, and near the source was Scotland's

Mill at Scotland's Bridge, which had been out of use for many years, but where the dam could still be seen at the junction of Townend and Pocknave Burns. The lade could also be traced down to the bridge where the mill stood. The miller's name was Scotland, hence the designation of the bridge and the mill. The latter stood on the Craigie side of the burn, which is the parish boundary .

MILLBURN MILL

This mill, which is about half-a-mile to the east, was occupied by a family of the name of Andrew. When Robert Burns was in Lochlea, a boy called Robert Andrew was running about the mill. He grew to be a giant in stature and strength, and decided to join the army, his choice being the Scots Greys; but a horse could not be found to carry his weight, and he had perforce to continue his trade as a miller - the *Muckle Miller of Millburn.*

A farm attached to the mill was carried on by a brother, and the two were in the habit of going to Kilmarnock on Saturday nights. One night they went into an inn where a company of Highlanders was billeted and became involved in a quarrel. They slipped away into the dark, but were not far on the road when they realised that they were being followed. Reaching an old ruined cottage by the roadside near Shortless, they took shelter, and securing a piece of timber from the roof for a weapon, they awaited the attack. Numbers were heavily against them but

The millar was of manly mak
to melt him wes na mowis;
Thair dirst nocht ken cum him to tak
so nowit he thair nowis.

"A Wee Faster"

The fight began, the heroes defending themselves as best they could. The muckle miller struck hard. Each time he got in a blow a highlander went down for the count. His brother, hard pressed called to him: " A wee faster man, Bob, and no just sae heavy." However, the opposition were too many for them, and the brothers were forced to retire through the house and make across the fields to Millburn.

Next morning the muckle miller was turning the kiln with his wooden shovel when he saw a highlander's head pop up through the hatch, and be as quickly withdrawn. Scenting danger, he ran to the hatch with his shovel, and was in time to hear the report of the highlander to his comrades; "She'll be a pig ane."

The enemy decided on a frontal attack and crowded the stair, but when the first head appeared the miller's shovel came down on it sending the lot in a heap on the floor below. Running along the kiln he escaped to the fields, and made for the Tarbolton Moss, where he lay low until the trouble was past. The muckle miller lived to be an old man, and died in retirement about the middle of the nineteenth century.

A Lake Dwelling.

Millburn Mill was acquired by the Duke of Portland along with other lands on the barony of Kylesmuir about the end of the eighteenth century, About 1856 the Duke decided to drain Lochlee Loch, the source of the water supply of the mill, and relieve the farmers of thirlage to the mill by closing it down. The final drainage was not carried out until 1878-79, when a crannog or lake dwelling was discovered, a full account of which was given in Munro's *Ancient Scottish Lake Dwellings.*[5] A family of the name of Allan were the last in possession of the mill.

FAIL MILL[6]

Driven by water from the loch formed on the Water of Fail, this mill only worked in winter as the water receded to its natural channel in summer. It was the introduction of a steam engine which first allowed all year milling. The loch has since been drained.

Fail Mill, Tarbolton

MONK'S MILL

At the lower end of Fail Loch in 1944 the writer found all that remained of the Monk's Mill, consisting of the foundation of the kiln, which had been a round one, and part of the wall of the corn loft standing about one hundred yards above the existing building. The old mill was taken down to open up a flagstone quarry from which the stones were taken for estate repairs. From the study of the ruin it was concluded that the mill must have been in use at a very early date and seemed to be Scandinavian in design, as it was constructed in a style similar to the type used at one time in the Orkney Islands.

In Timothy Pont's map of about 1600, the loch is shown as roughly one hundred yards shorter than it was before it was drained At some time a course had been cut for the water from almost the head of the loch to the building existing in 1944. There a bridge was built to take cart traffic, and it also supported three sluices for retaining the water on the meadows, thereby giving a sufficient supply of power to the mill in winter.

Water Fowls' Haunt

These sluices were withdrawn on April 1 to allow the hay to grow on the meadows, and closed again on October 1. In 1848 the bed of the river was lowered by about three feet, another bridge built and the number of sluices increased to six. The loch was about threequarters of a mile long and half a mile broad; at the deepest part it was about five feet. This was a favourite place for many water fowl.

In 1858 the mill was completely renewed by raising the building and installing new machinery supplied by Messrs J. and A. Taylor, engineers, Ayr. Three pairs of stones, in line, were put in the mill, and this work was supervised by Mr James Andrew, Barskimming Mill, Mauchline. An inventor himself, he put some of his own ideas into the reconstruction. The meal sieve was of three sheets -Nos. 9, 10 and 11 - the last one being "black japanned." As there was no water power for summer work a steam engine was introduced. Fuel was exceedingly cheap, as is seen in 1885, when good coal dross could be had at Caprington for two shillings per ton, and was later reduced to 1s 10d in an attempt to increase the sale.

It is of interest to note that, whilst Burns was in Lochlea, John Andrew was miller here - a bit of a poet himself, he was an intimate friend of the Bard.

A Night Incident.

There is no record of loss of life in this loch although it was well patronised by skaters and curlers in winter. Two narrow escapes were, however, known to the author. The first concerns one of the millers who knew that the retaining bank was of turf and apt to flood when the loch became too full and the bank became damaged. One night, after the miller had retired to bed, he heard heavy rain which continued for a considerable time. Thinking of the turf banking, he got up and proceeded to the sluices with the intention of easing the situation by releasing some of the water. Wearing only one garment, he braved the elements and with the lever raised the sluice about two feet, but, attempting to get the lever into the next hole, he overbalanced and fell head first into almost eight feet of water immediately in front of the sluice, under which he was drawn and forced through the bridge. Fortunately the river bed beyond the bridge was very wide and, consequently, the water here was not so deep. This enabled him to get a footing and he scrambled out.

The Ice Broke.

The next incident concerns a Tarbolton schoolmaster who came to skate. Instead of following the others who were skating along the side of the retaining bank, where the water was shallow, he tried to cross the main course of the water of Fail in its passage through the loch. As the current was running to supply water for the mill the ice was always thin, and he went through. Throwing out his arms, the current held him against the ice and kept him from sinking until ropes were procured to haul him to safety. Although the water was deep he was none the worse of his ordeal.

This loch was in the parish of Barnweil until that parish was suppressed about 1700, when it became part of the parish of Tarbolton. To secure both sides of the loch the farm of Redray was purchased by Sir David Hunter Blair of Brownhill towards the end of the eighteenth century.

The original Failfuirde was fully a hundred yards down the water from the mill and about the same distance from the monastery. Men repairing the road came on the pitching of the old ford at the bend of the road below Redray Farm. This ford was on the Monks' Road that joined the monasteries. The lands of the Mauchline monks came to one end of the ford and those of the Fail to the other end. With the drying of the loch, the mill ceased to function.

TARBOLTON MILL[7]

Better known perhaps as Willie's Mill, Tarbolton Mill, one of the best known in the world because of its association with Robert Burns was, at the time of the poet, possessed by William Muir. It was here that Jean Armour sheltered before her second twins were born and here the poet occasionally met Montgomerie's Peggie. A short distance from the mill, on the way to the village is where Burns depicted his meeting with Death.

Drained for Hay

The mill was driven by water retained on the meadow in the winter. Sluices were put across the Water of Fail on September 22 and withdrawn on March 22. The loch was about threequarters of a mile long and about the same in breadth. It was very shallow being about two feet deep in the middle. Like Fail Loch, it was drained off by open ditches in the summer for growing hay. In time steam was introduced to drive the mill during that period of the year, and steam later gave way to oil

About 1856 the mill was completely overhauled and renewed by Messrs. J. & T. Young, Vulcan Foundry, Ayr. A breast wheel supplied by a lade from the loch was installed and three pairs of stones were put in round a crown cog wheel. Robert Steven was miller then and was followed by Walter and Alexander Calderwood. The meadows - partly made by the flooding of the loch in the winter six months and partly by the silt settling there from the surrounding fields washed down by the rains, were possessed by six or seven farmers who grazed or cut them for hay. The silt was good manure and the hay always best and heaviest where the water was at its deepest.

Curlers' Joy

The loch was a great asset to the village and surrounding area. When winter muffled up his cloak, there was plenty of scope for skaters and curlers. If the frost lasted for a spell and the mill kept drawing the water from beneath the ice and if the ice over the ditches remained strong enough, a curling stone, coming at high speed, caused a roar like thunder. Perhaps a poet from Tarbolton was thinking of that when, before playing a Kilmarnock club, he wrote a few verses - one being:

> *Kilmarnock boys throw up your stones,*
> *Be sure and guard the winner;*
> *for, if Jock Shirlaw sees an inch,*
> *Awa' it goes like thunner.*

(John Shirlaw was a famous curler in the 1870's)

When the inter-parish matches came on, goodly crowds were there to see them and, on a Saturday, it was well patronised by skaters. The loch was so shallow that there was no danger provided one kept off the main course of the Water of Fail, and this was easily seen because it banked making it look as if there were two lochs.

The river was very level, not much of a fall on it and consequently it twisted about to form pools where there were a few trout and lots of eels. The sharp-nosed eel, which is the best for eating, was to be found in plenty. The shovel-nosed eel was also found, but was not of much use for the table as the flesh is coarse. A sharp-nosed eel has been seen to put its nose into a knot hole in a sluice, push its way through the hole to come down on the bed of the river with a flop and hurry down stream, in all probability on its way to the Atlantic where it has its young and they, in turn, come back to the rivers in shoals. The shovel-nosed does not go out to sea but keeps in the estuaries of the rivers.

There was a peat moss where some of the farmers had a right to cut the peat for their own use, but that was later abandoned as plenty of coal could be had in the neighbourhood.

Dry Without Benefit.

Tarbolton Mill was one of the mills which disappeared as a working proposition because of the desire on the part of the tenants of the meadows to have them drained and ploughed for cropping. For many years the farmers desired this, and, following a petition to do away with the mill, Lord Howard de Walden bought it and suppressed it towards the end of the 1914-18 War. The building of the sluices was cleared and the bed of the river at and below the sluices deepened. A start was made to clean the Water of Fail from Scotland's Bridge to Parkmill Dam - about four and a half miles - by using a mechanical navvy. The main course and many of the larger ditches were cleaned but, with it all, Tarbolton Loch was dry by the 1920's with no apparent benefit to the meadows.

Earlier an explanation of the term *multure* was given, and it is interest to note that, in 1850, only one farm paid multure to Willie's Mill and it was in money - £2. 2/-. The landlord was liable for the payment but he often added an amount to the rent of the tenant to cover this.

PARK MILL

About a mile below Tarbolton Mill was Park Mill, at one time on the estate of Park Place - a house which had completely disappeared by the 1940's and was possessed, at an early date, by a branch of the Muirs of Rowallan, to be later acquired by the Montgomeries of Coilsfield. This mill was a flax and meal one with one pair of stones. Later, the water wheel was used for a sawmill and finally for farm work. The mill was blown up in 1943 with explosives when the river was being cleaned and deepened. In 1850, Parkmill was occupied by Andrew Harvie, a farmer and tilemaker.

FAILFORD MILL

Nearer the mouth of the Water of Fail, is the village of Failford, and here was a meal mill driven by the water from a tributary of the Fail - Yonderton Burn. The mill was closed about the beginning of the nineteenth century and was then used for sawing wood used in the making of cases for Water of Ayr hones. In 1850, George Imery was in possession when the mill was converted into a dwelling house - the fourth generation of the family was there in 1944. The house is now named Ladehead, but is still best known as Failford Sawmill. It is the last of the six mills once located on the Water of Fail. Four of them had only one pair of stones, and therefore the output of meal was not large, whereas Fail and Tarbolton mills each had three pairs and were better equipped in other ways. Fail had a large kiln capable of drying sixty bags of corn per day, whilst Willie's Mill could only produce forty bags. The four small mills had perforated clay tiles on the kilnhead but the two large mills had cast-iron plates.

THE RIVER COYLE [8]

Near the junction of the Coyle with the Water of Ayr was Barclaugh Mill, whilst about a mile further up was Mill o' Ness, and not far from the road to Ochiltree was Trabboch Mill. Situated a mile and a half further on was Millmannoch; about another mile beyond, near Barbieston, was Mill o' Shiel, and below Rankinston was Littlemill.

LITTLEMILL

This mill was on the upper reaches of the river, was driven by a breast wheel and had a pair of stones. It gave its name to the district, the school and a road which was intended as a main road to open up the centre of Ayrshire from the seaport of Irvine. This road was through Dundonald, Tarbolton, Stair and Drongan to Littlemill and was called the Irvine-Littlemill road.

The writer remembered the new granite mile stones being put up on this road. Mr Campbell, the retiring road surveyor, and Mr Allan Stevenson, the new surveyor, did the measuring about the year 1878 - some of them were removed in the 1940's. Previous to the granite, the mile stones were sandstone and very exact in the measurements, down to yards, and some of them were used to repairing the foundation of the piers of Stair bridge.

MILL O' SHIEL

When Robert Bruce was reigning he tried to encourage tradesmen, merchants and farmers from the continent to settle in Scotland in an attempt to improve the country. A family of the name of Rankin, a Fleming, acquired the lands of Shield and called it Shiel Rankin, comprising Shielhill (now Shiel), Shiel Mains, Shiel Loch, Shiel Mill and Shiel House. An old house with crow stepped gables, close behind Drongan House and communicating with it may have been the old House of Shiel or its successor. Nearly the whole of the Shiel estate was incorporated with that of Drongan. A medium sized farm was attached to the mill and was still named Mill o' Shiel.

Mill o' Shiel was one of the old mills, and must have been in operation at a very early date. It may have been built shortly after Rankin acquired the lands of Shiel as the mill was marked on early maps. When it ceased to function it still had the wooden gears and the clay perforated kiln head. The weir was about three quarters of a mile up the river. The lade, in its course, was joined by the Lane or Taglum burn, and also brought the water from Loch Shiel when that loch was in existence. The water power was good, as a retaining dam for collecting the water was close to the mill. One pair of Kameshill stones was in the mill, which did all the shelling of oats and finishing of oatmeal.

Tragedy

On February 4, 1866, the miller, George Anderson, set out for Ayr Fair. With him, in the cart, were his wife and ploughman, named Grieve. The river passed within thirty yards of the mill and the crossing, at that time, was through a ford. The water was low and all was well. About mid-day, the rain came on and the river commenced to rise. By the time they reached Barbieston, on the return journey, the flow was becoming heavy.

Turning in for the ford, he was advised by Mr McIntyre and others not to attempt a crossing. They desired him to stable his horse in the joiner's stable, go home by the footbridge and return for the horse and cart on the following morning when the river, no doubt, should have fallen. The miller, however, said that he would view the water himself as he had a "mark" in the form of a stone which, if covered by the water, told him the crossing was dangerous, but, if the stone showed six inches above the water, the crossing was safe. Seeing the stone above the water, he decided to take the risk and hurried back to the cart.

Fatal Ten Minutes

Before he had got down again to the ford he had lost ten minutes or thereabouts; but the river has been known to rise a foot in a few minutes. Without a halt they drove on to the ford, sitting at the near side, facing the current, which was the wrong side to sit. The river was now running at a very high speed and the horse, being young, became restive and began to plunge about. It lost its footing and fell. The cart pins had no lockers.

The horse and cart were now in Millmannoch Dam and in deeper water, but the animal managed to swim to the side and get its fore feet up on the bank where it was low behind the old mill; but the current caught the cart and carried it round, drawing the horse with it and then it was seen being carried over the pitching of the dam. It was carried out to sea and washed on the sands between Prestwick and Ayr. One of the men was found about a mile and a half from the ford caught on the branch of a tree, whilst the other was carried further down. After a long search the miller's wife was found washed in below the bank near Cairnston. They were buried in Coylton Churchyard and a stone erected to their memory.

Some time after this tragedy an iron bridge was built to carry the traffic, just below the ford, and in 1904 another bridge was erected about a mile lower down the river at Millmannoch. The "brawling Coyle" was well supplied with bridges on this reach of its water.

MILLMANNOCH[9]

Millmannoch or Kilmanoch - the cell of the monk - was in the barony of Sundrum and was possessed in 1373 by Sir Duncan Wallace, who had also the barony of Dalmellington. He was married to Eleanor Bruce, Countess of Carrick, but died without issue and was succeeded by his nephew Sir Allan Cathcart, who through his mother succeeded to the barony of Auchincruive, thus uniting it with Sundrum and Dalmellington. By 1713, much of the land had been sold and what was left was united into one free barony under the name of Cathcart. Millmannoch was still retained, being the barony mill and, at that time, holding a large amount of multures.

Milmannoch Mill

The Original Trysting Thorn at Milmannock Mill

The sale of the barony of Cathcart by Charles Shaw of Sauchrie, Lord Cathcart, was in 1758. It was bought by James Murray of Broughton. The new owner sold the Sundrum part to John Hamilton and it remained with that family for one hundred and fifty five years - *the Miln of Milnmannoch with miln lands, multures sucen and sequels of the same.* The lands of Milnmannoch and Bankhead, all possessed by John Morton, were a detached part and were included in the sale to John Hamilton. The weir, on the Water of Coyle, was at Mill o' Shiel. The old water wheel there used to discharge its water into Millmannoch Dam from which a lade conducted the water to the retaining dam above the mill at Millmannoch. From there the power was regulated to the water wheel.

Trysting Thorn (new growth)

Up to 1884, the old gears and breast wheel were still in use but a new iron bucket "overshot" was put in with new gear for one pair of stones. This, however, was found to be unsatisfactory and in 1902 the whole machinery was again cleared out, including the water wheel, and a Hercules turbine installed having a speed of 450 revolutions and, at the "gate," when fully opened, 600 cubic feet of water per minute. The water supply was by means of one 21in. diameter pipe. The drive on the main shaft was by a belt.

Austrian Stones

The mill was fitted with three pairs of stones - one pair of Kameshill for shelling, one pair of French burr for finishing oatmeal and one pair "Eversharp" for provender. The last named stones were invented and made by Joseph Trapp, Pilsten, Austria-Hungary, and the first of these stones that arrived in Scotland came to this mill. The stone was first cooked in ovens, then broken and stamped down till about the size of rough sawdust. It was then mixed with liquid cement, put into a mould and pressed like a cheese in a chisset. It was more easily made than the older stones and was consequently much cheaper. It was also more easily maintained and made a satisfactory job.

The lade from the weir at Mill o' Shiel was about threequarters of a mile long and, whilst cleaning it, three stone axes were found. One of them was flint of the *Doggerbank* or *Grime's Graves* class. This was well shaped, rounded on the face with the other end narrow and had been sharp. Archaeologists cleaned two or three of the so-called graves or holes and proved that they were dug to procure flint for making axes and other sharp tools many thousands of years ago. Near Thetford, there are hundreds of these pits still to open and be examined. The travel down the river made the axe rough. On the flat it was seven inches long and three at the face. It may have been moving down the river when King Coyle was crossing at Knockmurran with his army of Britons.

At the beginning of the eighteenth century this mill was occupied by a family called Kilpatrick, who also carried on the trade of blacksmith. At that time, milling lasted about seven months of the year - September to April - and, consequently, millers had to look for other work for the remainder of the year. Early in the twentieth century, part of the smithy was still standing and, in front of it, there was a large boulder of granite sunk to the level of the ground with a *dog* fixed into it for turning cart wheel shods.

Handsome Nell

Here Allan Kilpatrick was born on October 4, 1725. He removed to Percluan with his father and followed him in the carrying on the two trades. He was the father of handsome Nell of the first song by Burns. Over the hill to Mount Oliphant was no great distance, being about one and a half miles.

This is the mill of the *Soldier's Return* by Burns. We often see a highlander pictured as the returning soldier, but this was not the highlander. Instead it was a soldier of the Royal North British Fusiliers that the poet wished to honour in this ballad. Depot No 1 of the regiment was in Ayr and No 2 in Dumfries. The soldiers generally took their discharge at Dumfries and found their own way home. Burns sometimes met them in or about Brownhill Inn, had conversation with them and so he pictured the scene on the Coyle. He knew the road well, having been seen passing the mill on several occasions.

John Thom was in possession of the mill at that time and he used to tell of seeing Burns standing on the road viewing the surrounding country. The route taken by the poet was described very accurately. Going in, near Coalhall, he took a straight line for the footbridge at Cainstone - an abutment of the old bridge was still standing at the time of writing. From there, he stepped into the glen he describes as bonnie and about one hundred yards found him at the *Trysting Thorn* and, in about the same distance again, Nancy's mother's dwelling was reached. In the title deeds, it was call Bankhead. A few stones were all that was left of the house in the 1940's.

TRABBOCH MILL [10]

Sir Robert Boyd, ancestor of the Lords Boyd of Kilmarnock, had a charter of the £5 land of Trabboch in Kyle Regis from Robert the Bruce. It was held by the Boyds till their fall in the reign of James III. There was a Sir Robert Boyd a participant at the battle of Largs and his son, also Sir Robert, was a staunch supporter of Sir William Wallace. The Trabboch Sir Robert, the third of the name in the family, was among the very first of the Scottish nobleman who joined the standard of Bruce and continued to serve him until his country was freed from the invader by the ever memorable battle of Bannockburn where he was, along with

Edward Bruce, in command of the right wing consisting of the men of Kyle and Cunningham. For his services Boyd received large tracks of land including the Barony of Trabboch, which was a very extensive Barony, but much of it was disposed of by the Boyds before it was confiscated by King James III and was conferred on Boswell of Auchinleck by James IV. Trabboch Mill was small with one pair of stones of a very old date. The wedge was still in use for raising and lowering the running stone for the alteration of the grist[11], round or fine. This was about the last mill where the wedge was in use. The water wheel was of the breast type. The water came from a weir or dam some distance up the river Coyle. In the early nineteenth century[12] James Murdoch was miller at Trabboch. In 1868 Peter McIntrye was miller there. This mill was closed many years ago and the water wheel used for making curling stones.

MILL O' NESS

The next mill on the Coyle was the Mill o' Ness at Sundrum House, which was the barony mill of Gadgirth. The first notice of the mill was in an account of Duncan Wallace of Ayr in 1359. The lands of Gadgirth are entered : *for the said three terms from the festival of Saint Martin, 1357, till the sixth day of April, 1359, of the farthing land with the title of Gadgirth, which, used to pay 50/- for the assessed rent, and now held in tack by the Sheriff and of 50/- for the farthing land of Gadgirth which Reginald of Gadgirth for the same terms.*

In the year 1764 John Muir Chalmers granted to John Hamilton of Sundrum a feu right of the lands of Hillhead and Mill o'Ness which gave him the rights of the Water of Coyle on both sides. The mill was a short distance from the linn and the intake of the lade caught about two thirds of the fall, giving at the water wheel about fifteen feet of fall. The old water wheel when the mill stopped working was breast and had sufficient power for the mill - about twelve horse power. The mill was used as a laundry for a time then turned into a sawmill and a new bucket wheel was fitted. After working for many years a turbine was installed about 1905, and was used first for the sawmill and wood working machinery and finally for lighting Sundrum House. The Coyle runs through a rocky channel from the falls which can be seen from some of the windows of the house. Some time after Mr Hamilton purchased the mill he opened a quarry further up the bank and used the stones to build a bridge on the rock to give him access to his mill.

BARCLAUGH

Barclaugh Mill was on the estate of Cathcart. All trace of the building had disappeared by the 1940's, but the bank of the water above the mill was still called Mill Bank in the disposition of Lord Cathcart to James Murray of Broughton. It is entered thus: *All and Hail the Lands of Barclaught Mill, Lands of Laigland and Lands of Potterhill and Oxgang, some time possessed by William Dick, lying within the Parish of Coylton.* That would indicate that the mill was closed before the date of disposition 1760.

This completes the six mills on the Water of Coyle, five of them with one pair of stones, Millmannoch[13] with three pair and still working in 1944.

THE RIVER LUGAR [14]

The Lugar joins the Ayr at Barskimming Mill dam. Three miles up the river was Ochiltree Mill, whilst beyond this was Mill Affleck. Near the town of Cumnock was Green Mill, with Bellow Mill about two miles beyond the town. It is thought that the name Bellow may have been derived from the noise made by the water in its rapid fall thought the pass to the mill dam.

On a tributary, the Glaisnock, stood Burnside and Skerrington Mills, whilst Borland Mill was on the burn from the Black Loch. The Burnock, another tributary, presented its own mill. The two waters, Glenmore and Bellow, meet in the Bellow Mill dam, and after passing over the weir lose their separate identity to become the source of the Lugar. This is not an exceptional case of name changing in Scotland as exemplified by the Cairn Water in Kirkcudbright which is renamed the Cluden after passing over West Cluden Mill dam.

BELLOW MILL

About 1940 the mill dam at Bellow was washed out and substantially rebuilt providing every chance of resisting the crashing ice borne on the roaring spate. In from the sluice - at the intake of the lade and reached by a plank when the water was low enough - was a chamber excavated from the solid rock. This chamber resembled a smuggler's cave or a Covenanter's hiding place, but it was actually cut out by the miller's boys in the eighteenth century[15]. It was about four yards square inside. There was a rough fireplace with a tile pipe which carried the smoke up to the miller's kitchen vent.

A short lade conveyed the water to a breast wheel of about ten horse power. Originally the mill had three pairs of stones - one pair for shelling, one pair for finishing oatmeal and the third pair for provender, but after part of the mill was burned down only one pair remained. The oatmeal plant was cleared out and a hammer mill installed in the 1940's, solely for provender grinding. The mill was rebuilt at right angles to the steep bank of the Lugar and had three floors, the top one of which was almost on a level with the road so that all the grain came in on the third floor and all finished produce was loaded from the same floor.

BRIDGEND MILL

For some time in the first half of the eighteenth century John Murdoch was in possession of Bridgend Mill, Auchinleck, which was situated on the Auchinleck burn at the foot of the town. The burn comes from the Common Loch and joins the Lugar about threequarters of a mile below Auchinleck. Here John Murdoch carried on his trades as miller and millwright, until he removed to Bellow Mill sometime before 1760. He was the inventor of the cast iron pinion gear and had his first casting made at Carron Iron Works, Stirlingshire shortly after these works were started by Dr Roebuck. That pinion was later preserved for historical exhibition. Millions of these cast iron gears - much improved in durability and smooth running were in use all over the world. This gear must be looked upon as one of the major inventions of the eighteenth century. Machines of all descriptions to some extent used cast iron gears, but sadly the inventor received no reward.

Timmer Hat

John Murdoch's son, William was born on August 21, 1754, and on leaving school followed his father's trades as miller and millwright. When he was about twenty two years of age he set out for the Soho Works, Birmingham, wearing a wooden hat which he had made on an oval lathe that he had invented. He was interviewed by Bolton, Watt's partner at Soho, and happened to let the hat fall. Hearing the strange noise Bolton asked what it was made of. "Timmer, sir, timmer" came the answer. "Do you mean to say that it is made of wood?" he was asked. "Yes, sir, I made it on a bit lathey o' my own contriving."

Bolton thought that a man who could invent an oval lathe and turn hats he could wear was worth employing at fifteen shillings a week. The firm of Bolton and Watt finding him a talented and trustworthy workman sent him down to Cornwall to take charge of the Watt engines being erected there. He found strong opposition from another firm of the name of Hornblower, who were erecting the Newcome engine, and he had to give one or two of their workmen a good hiding before he got peace to continue with his own work. Performing his duties to the best of his ability he was highly trusted and respected by the mine owners.

At this time he was also working on a model of his mobile locomotive on which he spent all his spare time. Bolton and Watt did not encourage him indicating that he would never be able to produce an engine to run satisfactorily on the road, and desired him to give all his time to improving the stationary engine. He had already invented the oscillating cylinder engine for steam boats,

A Fertile Brain

At Coalhall, near Drongan, there was still in the 1940's the remains of an old building which had once housed a Newcomen engine. In the mid-nineteenth century it was known as the *auld engine*. It was used for pumping water out of the Drongan coal mines and was claimed to be the first Newcomen engine to be erected in Scotland.

At Fail Mill, near Tarbolton, up to the year 1889, there was working a Watt condensing engine with the Murdoch improvements. It was a crank overhead. Many people came to see it working. An engineman came in on day, and after watching the engine for about a quarter of an hour he said, "You have got a fine steady working engine, but," said he, pointing to the crank shaft, "what are the three eccentrics for?" He was told No.1 next the cylinder was the slide-valve, No.2 the force pump sending a supply of hot water from the condenser back into the boilers and No.3 the suction pump drawing the water from the water of Fail to the condenser, diameter eight inches. The boilers were pressured about 45 lbs per sq. in., and with the 14½ lbs. vacuum gave sufficient power to run the mill. The engine was scrapped in 1890.

William Murdoch was one of Scotland's finest inventors, although much of his work was buried in Watt's steam engine, as many of the improvements in that engine came from his fertile brain. He lived to be an old man of 85 and died at his house within sight of the Soho Works on November 15, 1839. A tablet on the wall of Bellow Mill dwelling house claimed that William Murdoch was born there on August 21, 1754, but it was also claimed that he was born at Bridgend Mill and taken to Bellow Mill when but an infant. Both mills were in the parish of Auchinleck.

BORLAND MILL [16]

Borland Mill was on the estate of Borland and in the parish of Old Cumnock. To the south-east of the site of this mill are three lochs: the first is the Black Loch, the next is the Little Creoch, and the third is Meikle Creoch. These three lochs are joined and the overflow from the last named goes into the Nith at New Cumnock, and then finds its way south to the Solway Firth. The other overflow from the Black Loch runs northwest and in about half a mile reaches the retaining dam for Borland Mill, where it was regulated on to the water wheel and passes on to the Glaisnock, the Lugar and the Ayr. It is evident that the three lochs stand on the summit level between Ayrshire and Dumfriesshire, forming an inland link of communication between the firths of Solway and Clyde. It is not impossible when the lochs are full for a fish to leave Ayr harbour, pass up the Ayr, the Lugar, the Glaisnock, and into the Black Loch, make its way through the three lochs into the Nith and reach the Solway at Dumfries.

The mill was situated on a short road of about threequarters of a mile long which joined each of the roads running from Old Cumnock to New Cumnock and made the mill very central. The building was of three storeys with a large sized kiln attached, and was capable of doing a good oatmeal trade. The drive was by a large water wheel of the bucket type, but in a dry time or in frost the water was very low and then a steam engine was substituted. Later a gas suction engine was introduced. The mill was equipped with three pairs of stones, one pair for shelling, one pair for finishing oatmeal, and one pair for provender.

The estate of Borland was for a time in the possession of a branch of the house of Hamilton. George Hamilton of Borland is said to have possessed Borland about the beginning of the fifteenth century. Hugh Hamilton of Borland on June 29, 1669, executed a procuratory of resignation of his estate in favour of his grandaughter, Margaret Hamilton, spouse of Hugh Montgomerie of Borland. He had sasine of the lands of Borland, Sannochhill, Smidieland, Rhyderstoun, Nethertoun, Midtoun, Watston, Stay, Borland, Head, Roddinghead, Borland Muir, and Callochhill, May 18, 1695.

In 1751 Montgomerie of Borland, with the consent of his son John disponed the estate of Borland to Mr Montgomerie of Coilsfield and Mr McAdam of Waterhead as trustees for their creditors. The estate was then sold. Inclusive of the mill it was the property of the Marquess of Bute in 1944. In the year 1851 James Craig was tenant of Borland Mill, but removed about the year 1857 to Privick Mill on the water of Ayr. He was followed at Borland Mill by John Henderson.

SKERRINGTON MILL [17]

This mill was originally on the estate of Skerrington and situated about a quarter of a mile from Cumnock on the Water of Glaisnock which rises near Glaisnock Moss and is joined in its course by the Borland burn from the Black Loch. The outlet of this loch is a little below that of Meikle Creoch so that in a dry time it sends most of the overflow from the three lochs down the Borland Burn which gave the Skerrington Mill a good supply of water. There was a retaining dam a short distance from the mill from which the water was regulated on to the water wheel which was of the bucket overshot type.

The mill of two stories was still standing in 1944 and judging from height and appearance it must have been one of what was called the broken-loft construction. Next to the water wheel about six or seven feet of the loft was taken out and lowered about three feet to form a millstone platform, then when the stones were down and running it gave room to fill the hopper by emptying the sack into it. The corn for drying was taken in at the kilnhead loft and loaded on to the kiln over the breast paddle.

John Henderson, the last miller in this mill, removed to Borland mill about 1857. Shortly afterwards the mill machinery was cleared out. At this time John Baird, mill-wright, Sykeside, took over the mill and converted it into a sawmill and joinery business, widening the water wheel to give it more power for sawing heavy timber. This family carried on the timber and joinery trade up to the 1940's. The country around being well wooded there was much wood available.

Sir Colin Campbell is mentioned in history as early as the year 1290 as having given to Newbattle Abbey a donation from his lands of Symonton in Kyle. David Campbell of Skerrington (or Skellington) in 1348 surrendered his lands for a new infeftment and was succeeded by his son Andrew Campbell. This in all probability was the Andrew Campbell who was taken prisoner at the battle of Durham along with David Bruce in 1346.

About the beginning of the seventeenth century there was a Charles Campbell in Skerrington and about that time the estates of Skerrington and Horsecleughe were incorporated and Horsecleuche became the designation of the family. George Campbell of Horsecleuche was returned heir to his father Charles Campbell in 1629. The property included the lands of Skerrington and the two-merk[18] land of Horsecleuche.

John Campbell, advocate, succeeded his father in 1725, and resumed the designation of Skerrington. In 1763 Mr Campbell removed to Little Cessnock, Hurlford, to reside and changed its name to Skerrington, the name of the old family seat. Dugald John Campbell of Skerrington, married on August 25, 1804, Janet, fourth daughter of the Hon. William Baillie, Polkemmet, and their youngest daughter was Mary Maxwell Campbell, the authoress of *The March of the Cameron Men* and other songs. She was young at the time and was staying at Locheil., After a long tramp through the heather with one of the family she composed and set to music that popular song. The estate provided the title of the law lord, William Campbell, Lord Skerrington. The Marquess of Bute acquired the mill, but in 1944 it was the property of a grandson of the first John Baird.

BURNSIDE MILL [19]

Almost in the town of Cumnock was Burnside Mill. It was driven by the waters of Glaisnock after it joined the Carsgarloch burn, which started about a good two and a half miles further up. This provided the mill with a good supply of water. Originally, it was a meal mill, but in 1868 it was occupied by David Earle as a sawmill and was later acquired by Messrs George McCartney and Co., who constructed corn mills, barn mills and all kinds of farming machinery. In the construction of barn mills they were known all over the country and even abroad, while many of the corn mills of Ayrshire were erected by them. George McCartney and Co., advertised in *Slater's Trades Directory in 1860 as manufacturers of peg and bolter threshing machines, barn fanners with all the latest improvements, steam engines, water-wheels, corn, flour and barley mills, upright and circular sawing machines, bone mills, liquid manure forcing pumps, hay and straw cutters, oat bruisers, turnip cutters, etc.*

Scots Patriot's Interest

James Meikle, millwright and miller, in the early part of the eighteenth century travelled to Holland at the instance of Andrew Fletcher of Saltoun, to study machinery as used by the Dutch in their mills. In 1720 he brought home and set up the first fanners. He also brought over a barley mill, which was the first used in this country. Both machines were a great asset to the mills and farms in Scotland, and soon were in common use everywhere. The fanners saved a lot of labour in the mills, as after shelling the oats previously had to be carried out to the shelling hill to get the husks separated from the groats if the wind was strong enough, which involved much loss of time. When fanners were set up and driven with a belt or rope from the spindle of the stones the work proceeded much faster.

Few of the mills had more than one pair of stones at the beginning of the eighteenth century, but many installed a barley stone at that time. Few of these, however, were working by the 1940's. The product was pearl barley principally for Scotch broth soup.

James Meikle had a son, Andrew, who was also a miller and mechanic. He was the inventor of the threshing machine. Born about 1720, he died in 1811 at Houston Mill, near East Linton in East Lothian. The first of the threshing mills was of the beater type of drum, and struck upwards carrying the straw over the top of the drum. It is understood that one of these drums was in use up to about 1885. The first improvement made was to reverse the drum and strike downwards, then the half peg was introduced and, following that, the full peg, and finally the bolter drum, which, if the power was sufficient was by far the best, as over and above doing the threshing it resulted in a more efficient job of dressing the grain. It left less for the miller to do, and delivered a better return of meal.

Social Occasion

George McCartney's mills incorporated many of his own improvements and were considered to be fine working machines. On the occasion when a new threshing mill was installed and about to be started at a farm the neighbours would gather to see it set away. The writer attended the start of his successor's mills. Mr McCartney used to attend all the local fairs and get in touch with the farmers, explaining to them the merits of his inventions. One day he told them he was working at the making of a buttling machine, which he said would buttle the straw behind their barn mills. No string was required as the machine tied the buttle with its own straw in the usual way from both ends. One of the farmers ordered a machine to be sent on as early as possible, but time went past and the fair came round again and the machine had not been delivered. The farmer went to the fair and seeing McCartney among a group of farmers he approached him and enquired why the machine had not been delivered. McCartney said the reason was that it did not come up to his expectations. The fault was it tied the buttles too tight, and there was too much time lost in opening them, so the production of that machine had been abandoned. George McCartney died in 1868. The works were continued under the firm's name by others, and for a time using the water power of the old mill. In the early 1940's, however, the building was converted into a trades hotel.

MILL AFFLECK [20]

Mill Affleck or Auchinleck Mill, situated on the Lugar about three miles below Cumnock in the parish of Auchinleck, was originally a meal mill, but later was used as a sawmill. In 1851, James Jamieson was returned as farmer, and in 1860 he was returned as miller. In 1868 Alexander Wright, sawmiller, was the sub-tenant.

This mill was apparently the barony mill. The laird of Auchinleck after the burning of the barns of Ayr accompanied Sir William Wallace as second in command along the high ground past Barnweil to Glasgow to expel Bishop Beck and Percy. On approaching the town, according to Blind Harry[21], Wallace addressed Auchinleck:

"Uncle," he said, "ere we these men assail
Whither will ye bear up the bishop's tail
Or with the foremost will ye gallop on
Kneel down and take that prelate's benison?"
Quoth Auchinleck: "I'll not ambitious be.
Yourself may take his blessing first for me.
That is the post of honour and your right.
I shall bear up his tail with all my might."

They were successful in relieving Glasgow. Thomas Boswell acquired the barony of Auchinleck about the beginning of the sixteenth century. He was a son of David Boswell of Balmunto, and was a great favourite at the Court of James IV, from whom he obtained a charter of the lands dated November 20, 1504. Alexander Boswell of Auchinleck, who became eminent as an advocate, was appointed one of the Senators of the College of Justice and a Lord of Justiciary in 1756. He had a great taste for the old literature of the country and had a fine collection of rare and valuable works. His son James Boswell, who succeeded him, was the biographer of Dr. Johnston. He was succeeded by Sir Alexander Boswell, the poet, who was killed in a duel with James Stewart of Duncarn.

GREEN MILL

Green Mill was on the River Lugar and the estate of Dumfries House below Cumnock.

The dam was cleared away by 1944, but the old lade, although filled in, could still be traced from the intake to the mill in a straight line, the tailrace continuing in the same straight line to join the Lugar and cutting through a loop of the river of a good many acres in extent. The mill stood on a level field and a full view of the buildings could be observed. The buiildings were unusually extensive for a country mill.

The water wheel had been breast which would require a large supply of water, but that would be available here as the Lugar and its tributaries have a wide catchment in the upper reaches, and only in dry weather would there be a shortage. The mill was a flour, oatmeal and provender mill. Four pairs of stones would be required with a Bouton machine of fine wirecloth for dressing and graduating the flour, also a smut machine for cleaning the wheat before milling. Sometimes the shelling stones were used for this purpose, but the Derby-peak stones were preferable.

The mill closed early in the twentieth century. In the middle of the nineteenth century the tenants were returned as William McGavin, senr., farmer and miller, Green Mill, and William McGavin Jun., miller, Bridgend. Later John Allan, grain merchant, was tenant.

The ancient name of this estate was Lefnoreis or Lochmorries, and was in possession of the Crawfurds, a branch of the Crawfurds of Loudoun. William Crawfurd had a confirmation of a charter from James IV in 1511 in favour of his son and heir, George Crawfurd, afterwards of Lefnoreis. The charter comprehends the four merk lands of Lefnoreis, the ten shilling land of Blackettle, and eight merk land of Beauch, together with an annual rent of ten shillings of the barony of Dalmellington.

William Crawfurd had a charter from James V dated April 16, 1633, to him and Agnes Crawfurd, his spouse, of the two merk land of Nether Beaux and the two merk land of Craigmain. George Crawfurd had a charter from the King dated May 17, 1539, of the two merk land of Nether Garraive and the two merk land of Dalhannay. The house and yard and half merk land of Garcleuch were mentioned on an apprising against Alexander Dunbar of Cumnock. William Crawfurd of Lefnoreis was mentioned in the testament of his uncle, Andrew Paterson in Burnhouse, within the parish of Tarbolton, dated April 10, 1601, as one of his creditors.

In 1696, Penelope, Countess of Dumfries, was returned as heir of entail to William Master of Crichton in the lands of Lefnoreis. The Tour of Lefnoreis was on the banks of the Lugar near Dumfries House. During the reign of Charles II, William, second Earl of Dumfries, acquired the barony of Cumnock, other lands were added and the estate became extensive. Many of the farms have since been sold, mostly to tenants.

OCHILTREE MILL [22]

Ochiltree Mill was on the Lugar, about a quarter of a mile from the village. It stood on a level holm, giving a full view of the mill which consisted mainly of one large four storey building. The dam was fully a quarter of a mile further up. Starting at the intake of the lade it crossed the river at an angle up the water and was very high with a long pitching at the back. There was also a breakwater wall and a couple of sluices. In the middle of the dam dyke there was a salmon ladder to enable the fish to climb over.

The lade which was a wide one carried a large volume of water down to the water wheel which was breast-paddle. The same water further down drove a sawmill before it reached the Lugar in the tailrace. The mill was well equipped for oatmeal, having a large kiln, one pair of stones for shelling, one pair for finishing oatmeal and two pairs for provender.

The mill was originally on the barony of Ochiltree possessed by the Colvilles as early at 1174. Robert de Colville of Ochiltree had a charter of the lands of Burnweil and Symington, May 26, 1441, Andrew Stewart, third Lord Ochiltree, was a strong reformer. He had four charters under the Great Seal of several lands and baronies, including the church lands of Ochiltree, between 1570 and 1592. The barony of Ochiltree having been acquired by William, first Earl of Dundonald, it was bestowed on his second son, Sir John Cochran of Ochiltree, who obtained a charter of it from the Crown on March 6, 1667.

Ochiltree was claimed as the birthplace of James Macrae, who became Governor of Madras in 1725. Along with his mother he left Ochiltree to reside in Ayr when still a child. He received some education in Ayr and was employed running messages and herding until he went to sea. After forty years absence he returned to his native land in 1731 with a large fortune. It is said that of all his relations only one sister was living but it is doubtful if she was a sister. She was married to a man the name of McGuire and the McGuires having been very kind to him and his mother he showered the most of his huge fortune on this family. The eldest daughter having married the thirteenth Earl of Glencairn, Macrae purchased the barony of Ochiltree and gave her it as a marriage *tocher* the price being £25,000. She was the mother of the fourteenth earl, the friend of Robert Burns. Some time after this the barony of

Burnock Mill, Ochiltree, 1960-55. *Courtesy of John Watson*

Ochiltree was sold in separate parts. The mill was sold as one property and was eventually sold to the Marquess of Bute. In 1851 John Murdoch was miller in Ochiltree Mill and in 1868 Andrew Murdoch was miller there.

BURNOCK MILL

The Burnock water, which is a continuation of the Black water rises near Benwhat and runs on to Burnock Head, where the name changes over to Burnock. It continues until it reaches the Lugar at Ochiltree Mill dam. About 2½ miles up stream was Burnock Mill. Close to it was a retaining dam from which the water was regulated on to the wheel which was an iron bucket of about ten horse power. In the mill there were three pairs of stones - a pair for shelling oats, a pair for finishing oatmeal and a pair for provender. The building was of three storey and had a medium sized kiln. In the 1920's the machinery was supplied and erected by George McCartney & Co., Cumnock, and was of the bevelled gear type. About 1840 Patrick Mearns was miller and farmer, and was followed in 1868 by John Murdoch, miller and farmer.

POLQUHAIRN MILL

Two miles as the crow flies south west of Burnock Mill stood Polquhairn Mill. The mill was driven by the water from the rivulet known as the Drumbowie Burn, which has its source at Knockaulderon and Greenhill and is a tributary of the Coyle, which it joins near Burnside.

A charter was granted to David Chalmer, heir to John Chalmer, junior, of Polquhairn, his brother, was served in the eight merkland of East Polquhairn with the mill and granary, and in the same month and year James Chalmer, Notary Public, burgess of Ayr, his father, had service of the lands of Waterside, Greenside, Richertoun and certain parts of the land of Wester Polquhairn. These Chalmers were of the Gadgirth family.

By 1944 the mill had nearly disappeared, but part of the lade could be traced and a few of the stones of the building were visible.

THE RIVER AYR [23]

On the river Ayr there were at one time fourteen mills of which only two were still working in 1944. These were Over Mill and Barskimming Mill[24].

The first of the fourteen was at the foot of Main Street, Newton, and was known as the Newton or Malt Mill, followed by the Nether Mill, sometimes named the Old Town or Burgh Mill, on the town side of the Victoria Bridge. Half a mile from Holmston stood Over Mill whilst a little farther up stream was Milnholm Mill and near at hand Dalmilling Mill. The next one was Privick Mill, and near Stair Bridge was Milton Mill. If we follow the river for a mile and a half we come to where Clune Mill stood, and about a mile and a half south of Mauchline was Barskimming Mill with Haugh Mill nearly half a mile further up stream. In the village of Catrine was the mill of that name, whilst at the end of Sorn village was Sorn or

Dalgean or Dalgain Mill. Fully six miles beyond this was Muir Mill, and above Muirkirk was Aird's Mill, where William Aird was miller in 1851. This was a waulk mill and no meal was ever made there.

MUIR MILL

All the farms in the parish were thirled to Muir Mill so all the farmers had to cart their corn to that mill for milling. Some of the waulk mills followed old meal mills and used the water power of them for their drive. Muir Mill was situated within about two hundred yards of Nether Wellwood on the opposite side of the river Ayr at the end of the plantation along the Sorn-Muirkirk road.

Of the mill and dwelling house not much remained in 1944. The weir, which was on the water of Ayr was near Wellwood House, possessed in the mid-nineteenth century[25] by Lord G. C. Bentinck. The intake of the lade was on the north bank of the river and continued along the foot of the bank below a house called Marchhouse. It then passed below the road from Cumnock to Muirkirk, and continued on to the mill - a distance of about half a mile. The lade continued beyond the mill.

Whether it carried with it the tailrace water from the wheel or not could not be ascertained at the time of the survey. In some places the lade was filled in and cultivated with corn. At other places it passed through deep cuttings and at one site it passed over a deep gullet with a burn running in it. It continued for about three quarters of a mile over the lands of Dalfram and finally turned in to the river bank opposite the old forge on the Auchinleck side of the water. This lade was shown on an old map compiled from estate plans by William Johnston, land surveyor, Edinburgh, 1828. The lade may have been used in connection with the manufacture of malleable iron on the Muirkirk side of the river. Muir Mill was driven by a breast paddle wheel. The diameter and width could not be ascertained but that type of wheel where the water was plentiful was very serviceable. The mill had one pair of stones.

As a source of income it was to this mill that John Lapraik of Dalfram resorted when he was in financial difficulties after the failure of the Ayr Bank in 1772. He let his land which amounted to three-quarters of Dalfram, and the other quarter belonging to Muir Mill was also let. It was the property of the Earl of Loudoun. John Lapraik had next to sell his land and even that did not cover his liabilites and he was imprisoned in Ayr. Whilst there he wrote a lyric *When I upon thy bosom lean* addressed to his wife. It was this song that led Burns to open his well-known correspondence with Lapraik.

A document dated June 11, 1777, concerning some property, was in the writer's hands and showed that before his financial crash Lapraik was considered a man of some importance. In the following extract from the end of the document will be seen names familiar to Burns enthusiasts: *Witness where of these presents, wrote upon this and the two preceding pages of Stamped paper by John Richmond, clerk to Gavin Hamilton, Mauchline, William Cunninghame younger of Caprington, John Lapraik of Dalfram and the said Gavin Hamilton.* This was a farm lease granted by Hugh Logan proprietor of Eshawburn to William Anderson, tenant. John Lapraik gave up his lease of Muir Mill about the year 1796, and died in Muirkirk in the year 1807. A cairn was put up to his memory near where he was born at Laigh Dalfram.

HOLEHOUSE MILL [26]

About four miles down the river Ayr from Muir Mill was Holehouse Mill. In 1646 John Campbell of Crossflat was returned as heir to his brother in Brocklerdyke, Holehouse and Sund, eventually Holehouse Mill. In 1851 James Struthers was farmer in Holehouse Mill, and Thomas Murdoch resident there. In 1868 John McCrae farmed there. Holehouse Mill may have been an oatmeal mill at an early date, but there is no actual record of oatmeal being made there. On this reach of the water there was a lint mill, a waulk mill and a woolspinning mill.

SORN MILL

Sorn or Dalgain was the barony mill of Sorn, and was situated of the end of the village near the church. The weir was a short distance up the river and the water was conveyed in a lade to the wheel which was a breast paddle. The mill was fitted with three pairs of stones for oatmeal and provender and was three stories in height. In 1851 the miller was Hugh Wilson; in 1868 David and Robert McNay were returned as millers and farmers; in 1890 Thomas Clark was tenant with William Gray as miller. Later the mill building was used as a creamery or collecting place for milk, but by 1944 it was a church hall.

The Keiths of Galston were the earliest proprietors of the Barony of Sorn. A daughter Janet de Keith, heiress of Galston, was married first to Sir David de Hamilton, ancestor of the ducal house of Hamilton, and secondly, to Sir Alexander Stewart of Darnley, both families closely related to the Crown. A charter under the Great Seal, dated 1406, confers the Barony of Sorn on Andrew de Hamilton, son of Janet Keith. It is said that at the building of Sorn Castle the labourers engaged had their option either of a peck of meal or $1\frac{1}{2}$d[27] per day. A peck of meal was then 8¾ lbs. James V when travelling to Sorn to attend the marriage of the daughter of Sir William Hamilton, his Chancellor, to Lord Seaton, when half way between Glasgow and Sorn, alighted at a well to refresh himself, hence the name of "King's Well," which the place still bears. Commenting on the bad state of the roads the King said that if he wished to do the devil an ill turn he would send him to Sorn to attend a wedding.

CATRINE MILL

About two miles down the river was Catrine Corn Mill which was also in the parish of Sorn. This mill is in a charter previously mentioned in this list of mills, but was also found in another charter. John Mitchell of Daldelling had sasine of that property with the fishings in the water of Ayr and the half of the Mill of Catrine on November 16, 1702. This family kept it for only about forty years when it was sold to a Mr Stevenson of Glasgow. Dalgain was purchased about the same time also by Mr Stevenson. Catrine Mill was a small mill with one pair of stones, but with a good supply of water. At that time there were only two families living there - the miller and the blacksmith. In 1786 large cotton mills were erected by Claud Alexander of Ballochmyle and David Dale, merchant in Glasgow. The water power of the old mill was acquired with the reservoir at Glenbuck being the source. The water ran in the bed of the river from the source to the dam at Catrine catching on the way all the tributaries - the Powness, the Garpel, the Greenock, the Whitehough, and other smaller burns. Another reservoir was made below the first one for the storage of a better supply of water. An attendant drew the water about six o'clock at night and it reached Catrine in time for the start in the morning - about twelve hours. If the water bed was dry it took longer to arrive. The Catrine water wheels were large breast bucket, each twelve feet wide and fifty feet in diameter. They were coupled and carried a heavy load of water. There was at one time working at Greenock a wheel twenty-two feet larger than the Catrine twins, but single. By 1944 these wheels were looked upon as water wasters as the modern turbine gave much better results. The second reservoir was dried many years ago and out of use as a water supply. Catrine Cotton Mills were a great asset to the district, increasing the population from two families to over 3000.

HAUGH MILL[28]

About two miles down the river from Catrine was Haugh Mill. Half a mile above the mill was the dam or weir. The intake to the lade on the north bank of the river started in an underground channel cut out of the rock and made nearly a direct line to the old mill, then continued on for fully a quarter of a mile to drive another water wheel before it joined the river near Barskimming Mill dam. In a plan dated 1828, three water wheels were shown following one another in this lade, the centre one being for driving the corn mill. All the machinery was cleared out long ago and after being used for other purposes the water wheel was also removed, but the circular recess in which it ran could still be seen be seen in 1944.

It was easy to see from the old building that it had been a corn mill. The kiln loft, still there, had been extended right over the old kiln and had been used for other purposes. A lade ran through below that loft for driving another wheel or for a bypass. The corn was taken in at the kiln loft and loaded on to the kilnhead over the breast in the usual old style.

In 1851 James Hamilton was in possession of the mill as miller and timber merchant. In 1868 he was returned as formerly miller at the Haugh mill, now proprietor of lands at Burnside, Mauchline. This mill was on the estate of Ballochmyle. A family of the name of Reid held the estate at an early date and had several charters. They were followed by the Whitefoords. Sir John Whitefoord sold Ballochmyle to the Alexanders in 1786.

BARSKIMMING MILL

Situated at the junction of the Ayr and the Lugar about half a mile below Haugh Mill and on the opposite side of the water was Barskimming Mill. It was originally in the parish of Ochiltree, but after the suppression of Barnweil in 1700 it was in the parish of Stair. The high dam crossed a little below the junction of the two rivers. The lade was large and carried a considerable volume of water. It was widened and deepened about the year 1834 and the road into the mill was cut and improved at the same time through the sandstone rock. In the old mill there were two water wheels and six pairs of stone, - two pairs for shelling, one pair for finishing oatmeal and the remainder for flour and provender. The two pairs of stones for shelling were necessary so that the process for making oatmeal could be performed in one continuous operation. The mill was of four storeys with a sunken flat. A large double kiln was attached and a fan introduced to force the draught.

Ingenious Miller

James Andrew, the last of the family who held the mill, lighted it with coal gas and had a ball on the first night that he lit the premises, but unfortunately the gas gave out early in the morning and the guests had to leave in a hurry in the dark. He also built in the upper storey of his house a pipe organ and procured the driving power from the mill. Being a musician himself he spent much time at his organ and on his retiral the instrument was sold to Mauchline Parish Church, where it was in use until replaced by a new organ about 1912. Having been in use in Mauchline for about thirty years it was later used in Patna Church.

One of his schemes was to use the wash from the byre and other kinds of manure in liquid form, so he got a tank installed near the byre and collected all the wash. A pipe brought the water from the lade to mix with the manure, a large force pump was erected and an iron pipe laid on to the field to which the hose was connected. The field was in grass and was cut for hand feeding. The pump was so powerful it could throw the liquid over to the other bank of the water of Ayr. This scheme, however, had to be abandoned as the forced grass proved indigestible to his stock.

A Burns Episode

Much of James Andrew's time was spent away from home supervising the erection of corn mills. He invented a lever friction hoist, a self feeding travelling saw bench and many other ideas adapted for mills. His father also James Andrew, was killed at his own sawmill. While standing looking on a strip of wood flew off the saw and struck him.

James Andrew's grandfather, also miller at Barskimming, knew Robert Burns well, both having courted Kate Kemp who lived with her father in the house at the end of the bridge. One evening they met on the bridge both intending to call on Kate, but her father's cow had strayed and Kate was away searching for it and had no time to go awooing with either Burns or the miller of Barskimming, so they both took a turn or two round the miller's holm, Burns using the time in composing one of his masterpieces *Man was made to mourn*.

James Andrew was succeeded in the mill by William Alexander, who had been in charge of it for some time. He introduced many new machines to the mill and carried on a large trade until it was destroyed by fire about the year 1893. A new and up-to-date mill was then built and carried on by Mr Alexander until his death, when it was sold to Mr Charles D Ross.

CLUNE MILL[29]

Fully three miles down the river from Barskimming Mill was Clune Mill. The dam and all the buildings had been cleared away by 1944 but a pool in the river was still known to fishers and followers of the otter hounds as Clune Dam. Here the old mill stood. Few farms were near it at the time of writing, but when it was working there were a good many - Coylsholm,

Moorside, Knightscross, Outmains, Crossbarns, Clune, Hillhead of Daldorch and others. The main road into the mill came off the Irvine and Littlemill road near the farm of Yett passing between Crossbarns and Hillhead of Daldorch and past the farm of Clune on to the mill. Another road came off the Mauchline and Ayr road at Outmains. These roads were very rough at that time, and the one into the mill very steep, most of the corn was conveyed on crooksaddles.

Clune Mill was on the estate of Coilsfield, probably being the barony mill as Park Mill and Tarbolton Mill were acquired at a later date. The mill had only one pair of stones and the meal was all hand sifted.

After the Reformation this estate was possessed by the Cunninghames of Caprington from whom it was purchased by the Montgomeries of Eglintoun, who held it to about the middle of the nineteenth century. An inscription on a tombstone in Tarbolton Churchyard reads: *This is the buiring place of Andrew Tannock, late miller in Clune Mill, who died March 25th 1785, ages 60 years.*

MILTON MILL

Passing down the river to near Stair Bridge we come to Milton Mill dam or weir which was built straight across the river. There was a break-water wall at the intake on the north bank of the river and two sluices to regulate the water in the lade which carried a large supply of water down to the old mill, the tailrace continuing on and joining the river opposite Dalmore and cutting off a bend of the river of about three acres in extent. The corn mill when it was in existence had the full water power, any surplus going to the other mill.

At an early date there was a lint mill on the same lade, and later a grass seed cleaning mill of Messrs. John J. Inglis & Sons followed by a hone mill of Messrs. Donald V. McPherson, and for a short time a curlingstone factory. An attempt was made to raise the dam dyke about the year 1893 for the purpose of increasing the water supply; but when it was still in its unfinished condition the river rose in flood, and carried nearly the whole of the dam away. It was decided to put in a concrete dam with a stone pitching and although the work men were being paid at four shillings per day of ten hours and the cement was costing less than £2 per ton the dam is said to have cost over £1000.

The water wheel was a breast paddle four feet wide and fourteen feet in diameter and the horse power was about fifteen. The mill was two stories in height with what is called a broken loft, the platform of which carried two pairs of stones, one pair for shelling and one pair for oatmeal which were driven by a crown cog-wheel. One pair of stones for flour and provender were on the second floor and driven by overhead cast iron bevel pinions. The millstones were large, two pairs of French burr, each four feet ten inches in diameter, and the other pair of Kaimshill which were five feet in diameter, the runner weighing 1 ton 10 cwt. There was a bouton machine for grading and dressing the flour and a barley mill for pearl barley. The kiln was of medium size with a large corn loft and a breast for emptying the corn over on the kilnhead.

Milton Mill was on the estate of Enterkin, possessed in 1600 by William Dunbar, a branch of the Dunbars of Cumnock and Blantyre. David Dunbar of Enterkin is mentioned in a Crown charter in 1623. Shortly after that date the property was acquired by a branch of the Cunninghames of Caprington who held it until about the middle of nineteenth century when it was purchased by John Bell. After the dispersal of the Enterkin estate the mill and adjoining land were bought by the Water of Ayr and Tam o' Shanter Hone Works, Ltd. Dalmore, who improved the water power by installing a modern turbine. About the beginning of the nineteenth century the mill was tenanted by a family of the name of Brown. In 1851 James Lennox was tenant, and in 1868 John Lennox was returned as tenant. The mill was closed as a meal mill in 1902.

PRIVICK MILL[30]

Privick Mill, Annbank, c.1925

Proceeding down the river from Milton Mill for about two miles was Privick Mill weir close to Annbank House. The weir was very low and did not require a salmon ladder. It went straight across the river and was partly natural rock with a long intake lade at the north bank, which was also on the rock. Two sluices at the end of the lade regulated the water into the second lade which carried it about a quarter of a mile down to the mill. This lade was from ten to twelve feet wide and gave sufficient water to supply two wheels, one to drive the flour mill and the other the oatmeal and provender mill.

The two mills were built end on to the river and were close together with a passage out through. The water wheels were about fifteen feet each in diameter and fully four feet wide. Both were breast paddle and required about three thousand cubic feet of water per minute for full load. The flour mill wheel discharged its water direct into the river and the other joined with a short tailrace. The flour mill was four stories in height with two pairs of French burr flour stones, a smutt machine and a bouton machine, with a mixer and cooler. A kiln for drying the wheat was attached to the north end of the flour mill, which was built about 1860, and had but a short life for the flour mills were changing over to the roller process - invented by Crawford and improved by Muir, both Ayrshire men.

Privick Mill, Annbank

In Privick oatmeal mill in the nineteenth century[31] the water wheel was made entirely of wood. The axle was an oak tree about fifteen inches in diameter hooped with iron and with iron gudgeons driven in the ends to revolve in the bearings, which were whinstone. The arms were morticed into the axle with rims of oak and oak starts. The float boards were of alder. The main drive of the mill, the pit wheel, was also of oak and the rim was morticed to hold the wood cogs which meshed into the iron pinion on the spindle of the stone. The bridge, which was also made of oak, was hinged at the one end and lifted and lowered at the other with a screw or wedge. In the centre of the bridge was the footstep, which was of whinstone. In it the end of the spindle ran and carried the running millstone, which was five feet in diameter, all the shelling and finishing of the oatmeal being done with this pair of stones.

When shelling a dust sieve was used with wire cloth bottom of thirteen wires to the inch which scoured the shelled oats and extracted the corn dust before discharging into the fanners. When making oatmeal the meal sieve was hung up in the place of the dust one. It had three sheets, Nos.9, 10 and 11. Off No. 9 came the meal seeds, which were used at that time for ovens, the overflow of Nos. 10 and 11 falling into a set of elevators and carried up for treatment again. The meal that passed through No. 11 was finished and ready to bag.

The old Mill was only two stories in height and required the lowered platform for the two pairs of stones. The provender stones were four feet in diameter and were also geared into the pit wheel. There was a barley mill driven by a water wheel of its own. About the year 1858 the mill was taken over by James Craig, who started to extend and improve it. The oatmeal mill was raised to three storeys. Large storage was built and the machinery was increased to five pairs of stones. In 1850 Alexander Wilson was tenant, in 1860 James Craig, and 1890 Thomas Henderson. The mill closed a few years before 1940.

ENTERKIN MILL

Enterkin Mill was about a quarter of a mile north of Enterkin House, and was driven with the water from a burn which rises near the farm of Benston and runs south past Pierhill, where it is joined by a burn from Dykes. It then passes under the Pierhill bridge and enters the plantation where there was a large retaining dam for the storage of water. From the lower end of the dam the water was piped on to near the water wheel. The building was of two storeys and was well built and was used as a barn after the stoppage of the meal mill. The water was also used for a sawmill.

Around 1900[32] there was found a bar of wood with large letters cut out in block for printing the name *Enterkin Mill* on the sacks, and on an old map was marked where the mill stood. The water wheel, a new one since the stoppage of the meal mill, discharged its water back into the same burn which passes under the carriage drive and continuing on past Burnside and Crawfordstone joins the water of Ayr at the Enterkin viaduct. The mill was in use when the Cunninghams were in Enterkin.

MILNHOLM MILL[33]

This mill was entered in the disposition of Lord Cathcart at the sale of his estates in 1759: *All and whole of the Mill of Millholm with the haill multures sucken and sequels of the same together with the mill lands of Millholm. Millholm mailing and Bog, all possessed (tenanted) by John Gilmour and teinds[34], parsonage and vicarage of the said whole lands with the Tower Fortalice, Manor place of Auchincruive in the Barony of Cathcart.* The Barony of Cathcart was formed by uniting the parts left of the three Baronies Dalmellington, Sundrum and Auchincruive after much of them had been sold off previous to 1759.

At this sale the old symbols were used and read thus: *To the said James Murray and his foresaids heritably and irredeemably in due and competent form and that by delivering to him or them or his or their certain attorney or attorneys bearers hereof of earth and bone for each of the said lands, clapp and happer for each of the said mills, a handfull of grass and corn for the said teinds, net and coble for the said fishing, a Psalm book for the said patronage, and other Symbols requisite and necessary and this in no ways ye leave undone.*

The only hopper in the old mills was the one fitted on the cases of the stones. It was about four feet square at the top tapering down on all sides to about six inches at the bottom and from three to three and a half feet deep with what is called a shoe which fittted up to the open space in the bottom of the hopper and conducted the corn to the eye of the stone into which it fell for grinding. The shoe had an iron stud at the back on which it moved, and at the front which was above the eye of the stone, it was hung on two ropes or chains.

A wood block was fixed on the inner side of the shoe above the eye of the stone for the clapp to strike. The clapp was a cast-iron block about four inches deep fitted to a light shaft with a box coupling, which slipped on to the top of the spindle of the stone and revolved with the stone, the clapp having three club shaped projections, struck the block on the shoe three times at every revolution and gave a steady and continuous feed to the stone. A spring was used to keep the shoe up to the clapp and was fixed to one wing of the shoe and to the other wing was a rope with a ratchet fixed to the cases of the stone to adjust it on the clapp.

In his poem Burns mentions the happer and clapp:

> *Whase life is like a weel gaun mill*
> *Supplied wi' store o' water*
> *The heapit happer's ebbing still*
> *And still the clapp plays clatter.*

And again in the song *Willie Wastle's Wife:*

> *She has an ee - she has but ane*
> *The cat has twa the very colour*
> *Five rusty teeth forbye a stump*
> *A clapper-tongue wad deave a miller.*

Milnholm Mill was situated on the north bank of the water of Ayr a short distance above Auchincruive House. All the buildings had been cleared away by 1944 and little was left to mark the place where the mill stood. In an old plan of the estate it was difficult to trace as the plan was much defaced at the place where the mill stood. The dam only went half way across the river, not the only one of that kind on the Ayr. Another of the same kind was at Dalmore, Stair, but was extended fully across. The intake went through the bank at an angle and where it reached the site of the mill the name Millholm could be faintly traced The ford may have been here as there was a road on the opposite site of the river called *The Three Green Knights.*

The mill being in the best wheat growing district in Ayrshire a good deal of the work was flour grinding. It was sometimes called Auchincruive flour mill and part of the miller's holdings were included in 1944 in the farm possessed by the West of Scotland Agricultural College. The Cathcarts after having Auchincruive for over three hundred years sold it along with Sundrum and Dalmellington to James Murray of Broughton, Kirkcudbrightshire who shortly about 1760, sold to trustees of John Hamilton the Sundrum estate and what was left of Dalmellington. Auchincruive was sold to Richard Oswald.

OVERMILLS [35]

Situated on the south bank of river Ayr about two miles from Ayr and half a mile from Holmston farm on the Ayr and Ochiltree road, Overmills was close to the ford and stepping stones through the river. The dam which was immediately above the mill started from the intake sluices up the water at an angle then curved over and joined the north bank. The dam-dyke was high to secure as much fall and pressure as possible on the water wheel and the curve gave it more strength to resist the current of the water. A short lade conducted the water to the water wheel which was a breast paddle of twenty feet in diameter and about five feet wide and developed 30-35 horse power.

The mill was four stories in height and was equipped with five pairs of stones, three pairs on a crown cog wheel, two pairs being for flour, when the mill was working a flour trade, and the other pair for cattle provender. All were later used for provender. The oatmeal stone was driven by a counter shaft with heavy cast iron bevel gears, and the shelling stone by a belt drive. The oatmeal sieve was the usual Nos. 9, 10 and 11. There were also two sieves for extracting cockle and other seeds from the oats. The sack tackle or hoist was a screw friction of the type put into the mills over a hundred years ago[36] and was made by Messrs J & A Taylor, engineers, Ayr, proving very serviceable. The kiln was a good size, with a fan to force the draught, carrying an average of about a hundred bushels.

The drawback with the breast water wheel was back water, which could only be overcome by a long tailrace and that could not often be achieved. The turbine was good for back water as it did not harm the revolver to run it when it was deep in water. Although the river bed was wide at Overmills a considerable working time was lost with back water. The writer witnessed the mills on the water of Ayr standing idle for a whole week from this cause.

Fully a quarter of a mile past Holmston was the old road into Overmills. This road approached the mill from the opposite side from the present one. Holmston farm was situated until Richard Oswald bought it and for some time afterwards, halfway between the present Holmston and Overmills. Before the year 1646 Robert Wallace of Holmston and his spouse disposed of a small piece of land to the burgh of Ayr near to Overmills. This land was no doubt to extend the road from the then farm of Holmston to their mill. The exact site is on the left hand side coming in at the bends of the road. This mill was one of the two mills still working on the main course of the water of Ayr in 1944, the other being Barskimming.[37] Overmills was the property of the burgh of Ayr for over three hundred years. The tenant in the mill in the 1840's was Hugh Wyllie, miller, and in 1868 he still held the mill and land followed by William Wilson and then Thomas Steele, the grandfather of the tenant in 1944.

DALMILLING MILL

Here on the mill field was founded a convent by Walter, the Second. The mill field was a large tract of land, which was later divided into several farms. In 1229 Walter brought from Yorkshire canons and nuns of the order of Simpringham, who were called Gilbertines. They did not hold Dalmilling long, returning to Yorkshire in 1238. The convent and mill were then transferred to the monks of Paisley for a yearly rent of 40 merks to Sir William More of Abercorn in 1368. A feu charter by James second Earl of Abercorn is dated 7th June, 1648, *in favour of Robert Alexander of all the two merk lands of Boghall and all and whole the lands of Chappellands comprehending therein the lands of Dykes, Smiddyhill and the Mill of Dalmilling lying in the barony of Monkton and Dalmilling.* The mill and lands were held by the Alexanders for a considerable time as part of their estate of Blackhouse. In the year 1786 it was in the possession of George Home of Branxton. Mr Campbell of Craigie bought Dalmilling, or Milton Mill as it was sometime call, in 1790 from Mr Home. The mill was still in existence towards the middle of the nineteenth century.

NETHER MILL[38]

Situated on the side of what was said to be the old Roman road, which entered Ayr from Dalmellington and the south and later called Mill Street and Mill Brae, the Nether Mill buildings occupied all the space between Mill Brae and the River Ayr. On October 1, 1531, a charter of feu by the magistrates and community of Ayr as superiors, on the resignation of Adam Wallace of Newton, Provost of the Burgh, of *ane piece* of land with the seat and place of a miln was granted to the Prior, Thomas Stevenson, and the preaching Friars of Ayr for a mass for the soul of the late Hugh Wallace of Smithston.

There were two mill dams. The main one in front supplied all the water for driving the mill, and it had two salmon runs in it. The second dam was about eighteen yards lower down the river and was less in height by a few feet. A large quantity of water was retained between the two dams which formed a pad for the water falling over the main dam dyke. This was called the water pad dam dyke. It reduced the scour of the water on the foundation of the dam. Both were curved up the water in the form of a bow and were built of large ashlar blocks of free stone which appeared to be very durable. There was a new dam dyke built in the year 1816, and in all probability this was still the same dam in there in 1944.

The retaining wall with three sluices was close to the mill, one sluice for each of the water wheels and one for the bypass. The two water wheels were breast paddle, one about 20 h.p. and the other about 15 h.p. Although there was a large volume of water here the fall was low - only five feet - giving poor results. There was also much back water caused by floods and tides, especially when the storm was blowing up the harbour. The intake or front lade was very short as was also the tailrace which had a revolving heck to keep back the salmon.

The mill was four storeys in height and was equipped with five pairs of stones, one pair for shelling, one pair for finishing oatmeal, two pairs for flour, and the remaining pair for cattle provender. Later the flour stones were also used for provender. A Carter disintegrator was in use in the mill for some years, and during the 1914-18 war a Henry Simon grinder was introduced with a husk sifter. There was also in the mill a worm bean washer, capable of washing from two to three tons of beans per hour. The kiln was built end on to the mill and in the early days of its use the corn was taken into the corn loft from Mill Brae and loaded on to the kiln over a low wall or breast, each *melder* being stored in the corn loft until its turn came to be put on the kiln. A *melder* was the quantity of corn sent to be milled at a time. There was no standard weight or measure, but in some parts of Scotland the amount sent at a time for milling was sixty bushels, and that was called a *cast* at a later date. At the Nether Mill the corn was unloaded at the lower flat of the mill and hoisted up to a floor above the kiln head, and loaded from there on to the kiln. Eighty bushels made about the average load.

Meal riots occurred in the year 1816, when flour and other provisions rose to a very high price. Oatmeal was 3 shillings per peck of 8¾ lbs., and the colliers in Newton thinking the merchants and millers were holding it up for a still higher price decided to raid the mill. Most of the meal and flour was stored in the mill so they called a miller's mob consisting mainly of colliers and their wives. They crossed over at the new dam dyke which had just been completed. The miller's name was John Dinning. The mob first attacked the mill and granary and completely pillaged all the flour and meal and then they started to destroy all other stores. Beans and peas were emptied into the river. One lot tried to smash the mill by throwing up the mill sluice and starting the mill. Having done as much damage as they could at the mill they crossed back over to Newton and caused much destruction in the shops there. Only a few of them were apprehended. In the year 1740 a mill for the manufacture of steel, such as was carried on at Kilmaurs, was erected at the Nether Mill. The available water power would be the inducement. This may have been the time when the second water wheel was installed. The mill was sometimes called the Town or Burgh Mill and was part of the Queen Mary Trust[39]. In 1850 it was tenanted by A & R Smith, grain merchants, and was held by that family for generations. By 1944 the mill was completely cleared away, the dam dykes and the retaining wall with the sluices being all that was left.

THE MALT MILL[40]

> *He maun hae his multure*
> *He maun hae his maut*
> *He takes muckle goupins*
> *But wha can fin faut*

In the early days of milling before weights and measures were established the measuring of the meal was by the *goupin*, the full capacity of the two hands put together. Multures were not always alike but if it was one in thirteen, that was twelve for the farmer and one for the miller with a *neiveful*[41] for the miller's assistant. One farmer took his miller to court. His plea was that the miller's hands were too big. *You observe, My Lord, said he, the size of this miller's hands*, and went on to comment that the quantity of multure taken was excessive; but the sheriff pointed out to him that if the measurements were all taken with the same hands and was one in thirteen then he was being justly multured, and so dismissed the case.

John Slezer, who was Captain of the Artillery Company and Surveyor of Stores and Magazines in the reign of William and Mary, in the *Theatrum Scotiae* shows two prospects of the town of Ayr in the year 1693, one is the view from near the Newton end of the New Bridge. This includes part of the Newton or Malt Mill which was situated at the foot of Main Street, Newton, and was a large building built in the middle of the street and leaving very little roadway on either side. It was parallel with the river leaving a road about sixteen feet wide between it and the river bank, which sloped down to the water and was washed by the tide. The road went on to what was later the north quay but was in 1693 nearly all sand dunes, mostly grazing for sheep. The retaining dam and intake sluice was in Main Street near Weaver's Row, the lade running down the centre of the street to the mill and after driving the water wheel passing below the roadway into the river. The mill was three stories in height with a smaller building attached to the gable which may have been a shud house or oak husk store and is the last building between it and the mouth of the river in Slezer's sketch.

Forty-eight Freemen in Newton were said to have received their rewards for services at Bannockburn. They appear to have been in possession of the mill, for on becoming Freemen they pledged themselves to defend with the other Freemen *the Burgh Mill and water gang thereof with their bodies and, goods along with other liberties and privileges*. The mill was built towards the end of the sixteenth century and was in use for about two hundred years. On clearing it away and filling up the lade a fine wide street was formed which is Newton High Street. The Newton Loch, the main source of the water supply for driving the mill, was dried early in the nineteenth century and was later drained and built on. The old water course still passes below many of the old houses in Newton.

THE RIVER DOON [42]

Within a quarter of a mile of the mouth of the Doon was situated Doonfoot Mill. Following the course of the river from about another quarter of a mile was Alloway Mill, and just beyond the old Brig o' Doon was the Dutch Mill. Continuing for a mile and a half Auchendrane Mill was reached, followed in another mile and a half by Monkswood Mill, while fully a quarter of a mile above the bridge at Dalrymple was Cassillis Mill. Another mile up the river was Skeldon Nether Mill. Still following the river for about two miles and a half was Carse Mill, then Patna Mill and Downieston Mill at the village of Patna. This was the last mill on the main course of the Doon.

DALMELLINGTON MILL

Dalmellington Mill was on a tributary of the Doon - the water of Muck, which rises above Glenmuck near to Loch Doon, and continuing its course down the glen is joined by the Mossdale and other smaller burns before reaching what was the mill dam near the site marked on old maps as Dame Helen's Castle. Above the lade was a well marked Helen's Well. The intake with the sluice was on the north bank, and the lade nearly a quarter of a mile long reached the sluice at the mill very high above the bed of the Muck water. After driving the water wheel it fell back into the Muck water which passes through the centre of Dalmellington and joins the river Doon lower down. This would have been a good place for a turbine as a great part of the head of water was being lost. Only about eight or ten foot of the fall was being made use of, whereas three times that height could have been utilized. The water wheel was a breast paddle about two feet six inches wide and would develop from six to seven horse power The mill was fitted with one pair of Kaimshill millstones with cast iron gears and driven direct from the water wheel shaft.   Nothing of this mill remained by 1945 save a part of the building where the water wheel ran, with the two millstones still lying on the bank.

This was the barony mill of Dalmellington, possessed at an early date by Sir Duncan Wallace, who had a charter of the baronies of Sundrum and Dalmellington in the year 1373.

On his death he was succeeded by his nephew, Allan de Cathcart. These baronies were very extensive. When he succeeded his mother to the Auchincruive estates his lands and superiorities extended from the River Deugh to near Monkton. The first Lord Cathcart was created a lord of Parliament about October 8, 1460. He was succeeded by his grandson the second Lord Cathcart who with his two brothers was killed at Flodden on September 9, 1513, falling near King James IV. The third Lord Cathcart was killed at the battle of Pinkie on September 10, 1547. The writer examined the disposition signed in his own hand before Cathcart had left for the battlefield. The mill along with other lands was disposed of prior to 1539 according to a charter of the four merk land of Camlarg and Pennyvenzies and the Mill of Dalmellington by Duncan Crawford of Camlarg in favour of John Crawford of Drongan and his wife. In the year 1851 William Arthur, sen., was returned as miller; and in 1868 James Bell was returned as miller.

DOWNIESTON MILL

This was the first mill on the main course of the Doon, the dam was close above the bridge at Patna and still retained the water in 1945. The sluice and intake were on the north bank of the river with a small arch opening at the end of the bridge through the abutment to allow a passage for the water of the lade which could be traced down the side of the bank to where the mill stood. The tailrace could also be traced down to where it rejoined the river. The water wheel for the corn mill was a breast paddle. The mill was closed for milling in the middle of the nineteenth century, and a thread mill erected in its place. All was cleared away by 1945. The mill was situated in the parish of Dalmellington.

PATNA MILL

The dam or weir for the mill was just below Patna Bridge and, like the Downieston dam just above the bridge, it still retained the water. The lade ran down the south bank of the river. It was about double the length of the one on the Downieston side and conducted the water higher up on the water wheel. The water from the first dam bypassed the second dam so that the Patna Mill did not get the advantage of the full water force from the river. This mill was working as a corn mill up to about 1870, and afterwards was used for a time as a sawmill. Some of the buildings were still standing in 1945 and were used for the small farm which was attached to the mill. In 1851 David Sinclair was miller in Patna Mill, and in 1868 John Hose was returned as tenant of the mill and lands. The mill was in the parish of Straiton.

KERSE OR CARSE MILL [43]

Continuing down the river Doon from Patna for about a mile Polnessan waulk mill was reached. This may have been a corn mill in its early days. Fully a quarter of a mile below it was Kerse Mill on the farm of New Smithston and within a short distance of the Ayr and Dalmellington road.

The road into Kerse Mill was narrow and steep. Where the dam joined the bank of the river the intake to the lade could be easily seen in 1946. The mill was on the north bank of the river at a bend, the lade coming directly from the dam. After driving the water wheel, which was a breast paddle, the water passed on and joined the river lower down. Another burn passes the mill site and also joins the Doon here. It may have been used as a bypass.

The mill was the estate mill of Kerse, which house or castle stood on the farm of Ashintree about two miles north of the mill. The estate was possessed by a family of the name of Crawford, who had a charter of the lands of Kerse from Alexander III, and were sescended of the Crawfords of Loudon and held the estate for many generations. They were the leading family of Crawfords in Kyle, and were often at feud with the Kennedys of Carrick. Sir Alexander Boswell in his well known ballad, *Skeldon Haughs of the Sow is flitted,* depicts old Crawford of Kerse sitting at his yett waiting on the messenger, Will of Ashintree, with the news of the fight near Barbiston, Dalrymple, where the Kennedys were completely defeated and driven back over the Doon. The Castle of Kerse had disappeared by 1946. Only a few stones were left of the mill, the rest having been used by succeeding proprietors for building on other parts of their estates. The Crawfords owned other estates in Kyle and Carrick which had mills.

SKELDON MILL

Passing down the river from Kerse Mill for two miles and a half was Nether Skeldon Mill. There were two estates of Skeldon, Nether and Over Skeldon. The latter was renamed Hollybush and the other retained the name of Skeldon without the prefix. At an early date this mill was possessed by a branch of the Crawfords of Kerse. It was on the Barony of Lochmartnaham. The mill drive was a breast paddle wheel of about 14 horse power. David Tempelton was tenant of the mill in 1851. The mill was situated in a hollow bend of the Doon about midway between Hollybush and Skeldon, and was carried on for many generations as an oatmeal mill until 1868 when the water power and mill were taken over by William T Hammond, a nephew of James Templeton, carpet manufacturer, Ayr, who erected a woollen mill on the site for the manufacture of blankets.

The water power was increased by deepening the tailrace and carrying it about half a mile down the river giving it a fall of about nineteen feet at the water wheel. Several types of water wheels had been used since the mill was erected. A new turbine was installed in the 1940's with horizontal drive by Gilks of Kendal, said to develop at full gate 150 horse power. From the head of the dam to the end of the tailrace was about a mile. Thus, in a mile of the River Doon, full gate could be achieved resulting in 150 h.p.

CASSILLIS MILL[44]

About a mile down the river from the Nether Mill of Skeldon was Cassillis Mill in the parish of Kirkmichael and about a mile and a half from Cassillis House. The intake of the lade was on the south bank of the river. The water was conveyed by a short lade to the water wheel, which was a breast paddle. The tailrace continued to join the Doon about a quarter of a mile further down. The mill was closed for a considerable number of years before this article was written, but the attached farm retained the name of Cassillis Mill. The Kennedy family's connection with the estate of Cassillis dates to 1153. The title of Earl, now possessed by the Marquess of Ailsa, dates to 1589. Cassillis Mill and farm were alienated from the estate and possessed by a resident owner by 1946. In 1850 James Baird was tenant of the mill and lands of Cassillis and in 1868 he was still in possession.

PURCLEWAN MILL

This mill was situated about a mile and a half north-east of Dalrymple village and about half a mile from the Ayr and Dalmellington road. The water power was derived from Martnaham Loch, which lies between the parishes of Coylton and Dalrymple. There are also two small lochs the overflow of which runs into Martnaham, Loch Fergus and Loch Snipe. Only one burn of any size runs into the Martnaham Loch, namely Sandhill burn. The whole catchment is restricted and consequently the mill was often short of water. The intake was at the south end of the loch and the water ran in a lade three quarters of a mile long down to the water wheel at the mill. The lade ran parallel with the overflow of the loch, and the tailrace joined the burn at the mill which carries on for two miles before joining the Doon below Dalrymple. The mill was driven by an iron breast bucket wheel and the millstones were geared to a crown cog wheel. Two pairs of stones were used, one pair for oatmeal and one pair for shelling oats and grinding cattle feed.

This was the barony mill. In some of the old charters it was called the barony of Loch Martnaham which included many farms in the parish of Coylton and was in the possession of the Crawfords, a branch of the Loudoun Crawfords. It was later acquired by the Earl of Cassillis and in the 1940's was possessed by their successors the Marquess of Ailsa. Many of the farms had been sold to resident tenants and others, Purclewan farm and mill being among them. It was the property of Mr D Pickles of Skeldon Mill at this time.

There was a family in the mill when Burns was in Mount Oliphant about the year 1775 of the name of Kilpatrick of which the Burns character Handsome Nell was a member. In the year 1850, William Calderwood was miller, in 1880 Walter Calderwood, in 1890 Alexander Calderwood, and in 1940 Robert Calderwood.

MONKSWOOD MILL

Returning to the bridge over the Doon at Dalrymple, a record shows that a bridge was built there to the order of the Kirk Session of Dalrymple by David Armour. The order is dated January 26, 1725. The cost of the bridge was £76 1s stg. Following the course of the river, about two miles down at a sharp bend was the mill known in the mid-nineteenth century as the New Mill of Monkwood. It was in the parish of Maybole and a mile up the river from Monkwood House. The proprietor at that time was William Paterson. The water power of the mill was from a dam in the river Doon. A paddle breast wheel was employed. There were five pairs of stones in the mill, two pairs for shelling, one pair for finishing oatmeal, and two pairs for cattle provender, but the mill had been used at one time for flour. The two pairs of shelling stones were required to ensure a continuous operation when making oatmeal. This also required double elevators, double dust sieve and double fanners, and meant the corn could be filled into the hopper, passed through the mill at one operation and bagged, which saved time and labour.

James Dow, Junior, Alloway Mill, was for a short time miller in Monkwood Mill. and in 1850 John Goudie was miller, in 1868 Hugh Ronald and in 1890 Claud Ronald.

GRANGE MILL[45]

Situated near Grange House, Culroy, on the burn from the Milton springs was Grange Mill, which depended largely on springs for its water power. Ayr in the first half of the nineteenth century was dependent on the wells in the town for its domestic supply and so when it was proposed to put in a gravitation supply the Town Council arranged with the proprietor of Grange Mill to take a supply from the Milton springs. The miller was compensated by having a steam engine installed to augment the water power that remained.

The filters were built about four and a half miles along the Minishant road towards Maybole. Eventually the Milton springs were insufficient for Ayr town and the Council located Loch Finlas as a source of supply. During one period of drought water had to be pumped out of the Doon at the filters and blended with the Milton water. After Loch Finlas was brought into use less water was taken from the springs and consequently the quantity available for the mill was increased. The spring water had the advantage that is was not so liable to freeze. The millers said that when the New Year was past there was not much chance of the lade and the water wheel being frozen.

The high dam was fully a quarter of a mile up the burn, but was not much used. A lade conveyed the water to a lower dam above the mill and from there it led to the sluice at the water wheel which was the breast type. Passing through the wheel it joined the burn which continues its course until it joins the Culroy burn.

Grange Mill was two stories in height with a garret and had three pairs of mill stones, one pair each for shelling, for finishing oatmeal and for cattle provender. The stones were driven by a crown cog wheel. The meal sieve was of the usual three sheets and the mill was fitted with a sack tackle. The kiln was of medium size and sufficient for the work.

Judging from the name of the two farms near the mill, the one High Milton and the other Low Milton, the mill was there at an early date. The springs were easily harnessed and provided a good and steady water supply. The mill in those days was equipped with a water wheel of five or six horse power to do the grinding, all else being done by hand. At a later time when nearly all was done by power the output of this mill after the corn was shelled was about six bolls[46] per hour.

Grange Mill was in the parish of Maybole and in the middle of the nineteenth century the owner was Thomas McMichen Crawford of Grange. The millers were a family of the name of Ferguson. In 1868 James and John Ferguson were returned as millers there. They were followed for a short time by a miller of the name of McCall and then by Adam Cunningham, who was miller there for many years.

CULROY MILL

This mill was situated on Culroy burn from which it derived its water power. In its early days it was a corn mill, but it was first recorded in 1851 as occupied by J & W Limond, carders, Culroy. The next return is in 1868 and is James Limond, miller, joint tenant, Mill, Culroy, and also William Limond, miller, joint tenant, Mill, Culroy. Either they made oatmeal or a mistake has been made in the returns. Sometimes the mills were let on a condition that they were to continue to make oatmeal. However, the conversion from oatmeal to woollens was a common feature in the first half of the nineteenth century.

Culroy burn has a wide catchment on the hills between Culroy and Dunure. One feeder comes from Glenalmond and Glenbay, a second from White Craig and Beoch, a third from Brown Carrick Hill and yet another from Penmore. There would be ample water for a corn mill. The Culroy burn continues on past Minishant and joins the Doon near Monkwood.

AUCHENDRANE MILL

Returning to the river Doon at Monkwood Mill and about a mile and a half down the river was Auchendrane Mill just above Monkwood Bridge. This was an old corn mill, and was used as a sawmill later by Messrs. Gardner, timber merchants, who also carried on the corn mill. The output of the corn mill was not large, but there was a considerable trade in timber. To convert the water wheel and make it suitable for sawing wood it had to be made wider to furnish sufficient power. Some water wheels were extended from 3 feet to 8 feet. This water wheel was a breast paddle. In the 1840's the proprietor of this mill was Elias Cathcart of Auchendrane, who resided in Fife.

THE DUTCH MILL[47]

This mill was probably a corn mill in its early days when it was known as Doonside Mill. The dam was nearly a quarter of a mile up the river. The weir started from the south bank downwards taking a slight curve inwards to the dam, then turning outwards and round to the intake at the sluices. The bends were constructed to mitigate the force of the river current against the dam structure. Three sluices regulated the water into the lade, and they were fitted with reduction gears. The dam itself was well pitched out to the tail and a salmon run was incorporated. The lade carried a large column of water down to the water wheel which was initially a breast paddle and discharged the water almost directly into the Doon again.

In 1851 George Dykes was miller and grain merchant here. He was still miller in 1868, but left shortly afterwards to take up a grass seed business in Kilmarnock. The proprietor decided to rebuild the mill and install new plant. Robert Scoular, stone mason, who had the contract for the building, originated from a family of millers, and when the owner offered to let the mill to him, he accepted and started business as miller and grain merchant in 1870.

The mill was fitted with six pairs of millstones for oat meal, flour and cattle provender. Later there was erected in the mill a Henry Simon plant of flour rollers, but the milling trade at that time was depressed. After the repeal of the Corn Laws in 1846 there still existed a tax of a shilling per bag on imported manufactured flour but in the 1870's this was repealed and many of the mills closed. Other millers converted production to cattle provender. The Simon heavy the water wheel was placed a few feet out from the side of the river and it was driven from a sluice from the lade. The old breast paddle wheel was still in use but it was subject to back water when the river was in flood. The Little Giant turbine was not a water economiser. It was only suitable for places where water was plentiful, but it was easily installed and not so costly as some of the other contemporary types. A machine for making pinhead oatmeal was added to the plant. This consisted of several perforated cylinders revolving close to knives which cut the shelled oats as they projected through the holes in the cylinders. However. this machine was abandoned because it proved too costly due to the considerable wear on the cylinders. Another product of oats was flakes which was processed for some time at this mill.

In the year 1903 the old paddle water wheel was dispensed with and and a new Hercules machine installed as a replacement. This turbine was known as the McCormack patent and was invented in United States of America. There were several manufacturers of this type of turbine in America and in England and Scotland. It was a low pressure type turbine and required to be erected in a well with a false floor through which passed the delivery pipe of the turbine with only the guide blades and the revolver in the well. In this case, however it was placed in the iron case of a high pressure turbine and power output was lessened. Running at full gate the turbine had a capacity of about 60 horse power. When the mill was converted to an ice factory a new and more modern turbine was installed.

Two dates were on the mill, one when the new mill was started - 1870, and the other when the ice factory was started - 1929. The site of the mill was on the barony of Alloway and was the property of the town of Ayr at an early date. In 1946 the Dutch Mill was possessed by Messrs. Thomas Murray and Sons.

ALLOWAY MILL[48]

Alloway Mill was situated on the North bank of the River Doon fully a quarter of a mile from the laigh bridge. It was the barony mill of Alloway and was purchased by Charles Dalrymple of Orangefield in 1754. The first lot about 15 acres was called Dykehead Moss price £112, the second was Alloway Mill itself comprising Dykehead houses and yards west of the road from Dykehead to the Bridge of Doon inclusive of 8 acres 2 roods 10 falls, price £230. After Charles Dalrymple's death in 1787 Alloway Mill was purchased by David Earl of Cassillis.

The dam was about a quarter of a mile up the river from the mill. It was built straight across the Doon, and was exceptionally high. Two sluices regulated the water into the lade which carried a large volume of water down to the water wheel of eight feet wide. The mill was completely overhauled in 1903. The main machinery was bought from Messrs. Davies and Sneid, mill furnishers, Hull, and consisted of two hursts of two pairs of millstones each (four in all) with bevel gears - one pair for shelling, one pair for oatmeal, and two pairs for cattle provender. The mill had the usual oatmeal equipment and was capable of a good output. The kiln was floored with iron plates eighteen inches square and was loaded from a floor on the same level. The corn was drawn off the kiln with the sack tackle.

output. The kiln was floored with iron plates eighteen inches square and was loaded from a floor on the same level. The corn was drawn off the kiln with the sack tackle.

In the 1840's James Dow was miller in this mill. The principal work then was flour grinding, so when the miller thought that he was not getting sufficient support from the Ayr bakers he decided to build a bakehouse at the mill and bake with his own flour. James, who was born at Paisley, was miller in Dunure Mill before coming to Alloway. He was also a poet of some merit and was successful in winning the prize for the best ode on the marriage and the arrival of the Marquess and Marchioness of Ailsa at Culzean Castle on November 14, 1846.

Alloway with other lands was conferred on the burgh of Ayr by Alexander II in 1236, and was erected into a barony by Robert Bruce in 1324. It extended to four merklands with the town mill thereof, the Curtecan (later Slaphouse) burn with other boundaries described in the charter of William the Lion. The magistrates of Ayr were the barons. There was a moat hill, but no baronial residence. A separate set of books was kept for the barony. The barons had the power of pit and gallows like other feudal lords.

It was to Alloway Mill that Robert Burns and his brother Gilbert were sent to get their first education in the beginning of the year 1765. Campbell was their teacher, but only for a short time as he was later appointed master of the Ayr poorhouse. He was followed as miller by a young man of 18 years, John Murdoch. In 1880 Andrew Smith and Sons were millers here. In 1903 Forest was miller, followed by Messrs McGill and Smith.

DOONFOOT MILL

Doonfoot Mill was situated a short distance below the laigh bridge of Doon about two miles and a half from the town of Ayr. There was only one pair of mill stones in the mill which had to do all the work of shelling and grinding oatmeal, and in early times even flour, but before the mill was closed the grinding was restricted to beans and Indian meal for cattle feeding. The water wheel was a breast paddle with a large wooden axle and from there was driven the sack tackle. The drive on to the millstone was also direct with a cog wheel. About the middle of the eighteenth century a barley mill was added to the plant to cater for the barley grown in the district. Meikle introduced the barley mill into Scotland about 1720. A large quantity of pearl barley was produced at this mill, which was for many years known locally as the barley mill.

> She has gotten a coot, wi' a clavt o' siller.
> And broken the heart o' the barley miller.

From *Meg o' the Mill* by Burns.

The mill was about a quarter of a mile from the mouth of the river and when there was a spate and the wind blowing in from the firth it was very apt to backwater the wheel.

THE BARONY OF GREENAN

The first mention of this barony was when Roger de Scalebroe, vassal of Duncan Earl of Carrick, grants to the Monks of Melrose the fishings on the Doon. This was in the reign of

William the Lion. John Earl of Ross and Lord of the Isles feued the Barony of Greenan to John Davidson. The mill and milltoun were mentioned in some of the charters. After changing proprietors several times Greenan was acquired by the Marquess of Ailsa. In 1868 David Dunlop was tenant of the mill and land at Doonfoot. John Allan, grain merchant, Old Cumnock, was also a tenant.

THE RIVER GIRVAN[49]

There were at one time on the River Girvan and its tributaries fifteen mills of which only two were still working in 1946 - Bridge Mill and Bairds Mill. The first of the fifteen was Bridge Mill about a mile up the river from the harbour at Girvan, and a mile and a half up river was Baron's Mill and in about three quarters of a mile Old Dailly Mill. From there to New Dailly was three and a half miles to the next mill. Here on a tributary was a mill, Gittybeg, and a mile and a quarter up the river was Drumochreen Mill. Following the river for three and a half miles is a tributary from Crossraguel Abbey on which were three mills - Abbey Mill, Dean's Mill and Baird's Mill, A mile and half further up on another tributary, the Dyrock, were two mills, Guiltree and Keirs Mills. At Kirkmichael there was a mill and at Aitkenhead a short distance up the river there was another. The next mill was Blairquhan or Milton Mill two miles and a half farther up the river, with the Upper Mill some distance above Straiton.

UPPER MILL

The Upper Mill had one pair of stones with a breast paddle water wheel. The drive was direct on the millstones. The mill was equipped with meal sieve, fanners, and kiln. The millstones were got at Kaimshill where the best Scotch millstones were produced in the early nineteenth century. The firm that supplied the millstones was Thomas and A. Wilson, quarriers and farmers, Fencebay Cottage, West Kilbride.

Early in the 20th century an old resident in Straiton said that when he was a boy he remembered the last millstone coming home to the Upper Mill from Kaimshill. The distance was about forty miles and the millstone was about a ton in weight so it required a pair of horses with two or three men. Two days were spent in the home coming. A procession was formed at the village of Straiton with the fiddlers sitting on the millstone and they marched all the way to the mill. By this time there were plenty of hands ready to put the millstone to the place that the miller wanted it for dressing, for much had to be done before it was in order to do its work. It had to be faced and the furrows cut, the rind beds opened and the rind fitted so the the stone could be well and truly laid. That night generally finished up in dancing and drinking success to the millstone.

A millstone of the Kaimshill class in a country mill doing local work would last from sixty to eighty years if running on oatmeal as the face of the stones do not come much in contact. By the middle of the nineteenth century most of the mills were using French burr millstones, which cut more cleanly and lasted longer after being dressed. Kaimshill stones were preferred for grinding bean meal for cattle feeding. At that time, James McMurray was miller in this mill.

BLAIRQUHAN MILL

Situated near Milton House and about three quarters of a mile up the river from Blairquhan Castle was Blairquhan or Milton Mill. It was on the north bank of the water of Girvan in the parish of Straiton. The mill was two storeys high with a garret. The dam was a short distance above the mill and the water was conveyed in a lade to the water wheel, which was a breast paddle of three and a half feet wide. There was mostly a good supply of water. The mill was fitted with two pairs of millstones which were driven by a cog crown wheel, one pair for oatmeal and one pair for shelling. The meal sieve was the usual three sheets, Nos. 9,10 & 11. There were also fanners and dust sieve. The kiln was of medium size and was loaded from the top loft. In 1851 George Reid was miller in this mill, and in 1868 William Gilchrist was returned as miller.

The first of the Kennedys was the fourth son of Sir Gilbert of Dunure, and they had possession for over 200 years when they were succeeded by the Whitefoords. Sir John Whitefoord, Major-General in the Army, gave a charter of resignation of one half of the barony of Whitefoord commonly called Blairquhan on February 23, 1758 to John Hunter of Mainholm and Milnquarter (now Craigie House) who may have obtained the lands of Mainholm from the Wallaces through his mother. His son, Sir James Hunter Blair, 1st Bart., assumed the name Blair on marrying Jane, daughter and heiress of Blair of Dunskey, in 1770.

The old castle of Blairquhan was superseded by a fine mansion built by Sir David Hunter Blair, Bart., in 1824. There was in the kitchen court of the new castle on the inside a surround of monastic sculpture work taken from the old castle. In the entrance hall there were two slabs of stone, one the lid of a stone coffin with the Royal Arms of Scotland neatly carved on it, while the other was a tombstone with the arms of the Hunters on the one side and the arms of the Cunninghams on the other. The two slabs came from the Monastery of Fail. The baronet in the 1940's was Sir James Hunter Blair.

AITKENHEAD MILL [50]

Down the river Girvan past Blairquhan Castle and Cloncaird Castle was Aitkenhead Mill. It was situated close to the main road from Straiton to Ayr and within three quarters of a mile of the village of Kirkmichael. It was convenient to a wide district. There were many road junctions in and around Kirkmichael and it was in a good corn growing district.

The old corn mill was three stories in height with three pairs of stones in it, one pair for shelling, one pair for oatmeal and one pair for cattle provender. There was a dust sieve with fanners for separating the shuds or husks from the groats or grain with the usual oatmeal sieve, 9, 10 and 11. A small set of fanners was installed for blowing out the meal shuds which went in olden times for the making of sowans. Sowans was a dish made by soaking in water and fermenting a mixture of oat husks and fine meal and then separating out the solid matter. Aitkenhead mill was burned and was bought by D.H. and F. Reid, engineers, Ayr, who repaired the building, re-roofed the mill and installed more up-to-date machinery. The dam was close to the mill with a low fall, the waterwheel was semi-undershot and about four feet wide. The main drive was by sprocket and the millstones were bevel-geared, one pair French burr for oatmeal, one pair of shelling stones and one pair French burr for cattle provender. The other fittings in the new mill were a meal sieve, a dust sieve, and fanners for oat husks and meal shuds. More modern than the old, the mill was fitted with a sack tackle and a corn bruiser. The kiln was of medium size and was also renewed. Tenants in the old mill were, in 1851, John Willet, miller, and in 1868, John Willet, engineer, Aberdeen.

KEIRS MILL

This mill was situated in the parish of Straiton near Shankstone Loch, from where it got its water power, being the source of the Dyrock rivulet. In 1946 there was still a farm of Keirs Mill about a quarter of a mile from where the mill stood, but there was nothing left of the mill except a millstone. The mill was of a very old date. There were only one pair of stones in it and in all probability it was not altered from the cog and rung drive of the eighteenth century. The tenants were, in 1851, James Findlay, farmer, Keirs Mill, and in 1868, Robert McCulloch, miller, tenant of the lands of Keirs Mill and Hillend.

It was the barony or estate mill of Keirs. The ruined castle was the old residence of the Schaws of Keirs. John Schaw of Keirs was served heir of his father David Schaw of Keirs in the £10 land of Halie, together with the mill, also the £5 land of Dawyne and £10 land of Keirs. He was also served heir of John Schaw of Keirs his great grandfather, in the lands of Camlarg on February 1, 1623. He and his spouse had a royal charter of the lands of Keirs dated April 23, 1623.

GUILTREE MILL

Following the course of the Dyrock water for about threequarters of a mile it is there joined by the Dalowie burn on the left bank and about half a mile farther on by the overflow from the Barnshean Loch on the right bank, and half a mile down on the left bank is another burn joining the main stream. However, the largest volume of water is from Loch Spallander which joins the Dyrock above the head of Guiltree Mill dam.

The dam was built with a long slope from the south bank to the intake at the sluice on the north bank, the overflow being at the south end. The lade which was about a quarter of a mile long ran between the Dyrock water and the public road and conveyed the water to the waterwheel which was high breast. The tailrace which was very short joined the Dyrock here and passing on through the village of Kirkmichael it ran into the River Girvan about half a mile above Mackailstone.

In 1946 all the machinery had been cleared out of Guiltree Mill and the buildings had been repaired for the use of the small farm. From appearance the mill had one pair of stones with a direct drive on the stone spindle. The kiln had been built end on to the public road and the corn for drying taken into a corn loft from the road. That was the usual arrangement before sack tackles or hoists were in use but the road in this situation was much too high for such a configuration. After being closed as a meal mill Guiltree was used as a sawmill. Tenant in the mill in 1851 was James Henry, miller, and in 1868 the tenant was Hugh Arthur, miller. The mill was on the estate of Cloncaird, but by 1946 had been sold to the occupant.

KIRKMICHAEL [51]

Returning to the Girvan at Kirkmichael, on the north bank of the river was a corn mill and also a waulk[52] mill. Thomas Kennedie of Kirkmichael was served heir male to his father, David Kennedie in the £10 land of the barony of Kirkmichael of old extent, with the corn and waulk mill etc., on July 5, 1653. This corn mill was not marked in the map of the estates of Ayrshire. It must have been closed at an earlier date but the waulk mill was marked on the map and was a short distance above the Dyrock foot on the river Girvan. There was a sawmill worked by James and Robert Dunlop at Kirkmichael around 1846. In all probability the water power of one or other of the mills was used to drive the sawmill. In 1833, a female heir succeeded to this estate - Mary Primrose Kennedie. She married James Shaw, second son of Major James Schaw of Dalton, who assumed the name of Kennedy in addition to Shaw.

ABBEY MILL

After the Dyrock, the next tributary of the Girvan river is the burn which passes Crossraguel Abbey. The source is about a quarter of a mile above the abbey. There appears to have been a pond or dam near the source. A small meadow showed part of a turf dyke along the lower end, which may have been for supplying the Abbey with water. From there the burn ran to the back of the buildings of the Abbey and continued on through a low-lying meadow at Daltamy. It was here, it is said, that the fish pond of the Abbey was located. It contained carp, tench, eels and other fish. The pond was afterwards known as the otter hole. The Abbey Mill dam was near Baltersan Castle, which was built after the Reformation on the site of the old house of Baltersan. Johnson's map showed the burn running nearly a direct course from the Abbey to what was the mill dam, but by 1946 the burn followed the side of the road for some distance then cut across the meadow. All the alterations to the course of the burn were made to improve the drainage. The distance from the site of the dam to the mill was one and a half furlongs. At the mill the water in the lade was about fourteen feet above the bed of the burn.

The water wheel was a high breast. The bypass and the tailrace turned to the right; then turned parallel with the burn for about twenty yards before joining it. The mill was two storeys in height, with one pair of millstones. A road branched off the road into the mill and was carried at a higher level up to the kiln loft door. All corn to be dried was taken in there. The mill and millhouse were both used as dwelling houses by 1946. The tenant in the mill in the middle of the nineteenth century was Archibald Haswell, miller. In 1868 he was again returned for the mill and the land.

DEAN'S MILL

Following the Abbey burn for fully three quarters of a mile the site of Dean's Mill is reached. This was one of the Abbey mills. Two burns join the main stream on the descent, one from Broomknowes on the north bank and one from Glenside on the south bank. John Kennedy of Baltersan had sasine of the four merk land of the lordship and regality of Crossraguel mills thereof, the four merk land of Baltersan and Knockronald, the ten shilling land of Glenlucie, four merk land of Mochrumhill, forty shilling land of Drumochreen and the merk land of Whitefaulds on August 31, 1709. Dean's Mill was working up to the middle of the nineteenth century. In 1851 John Muir was farmer in Dean's Mill, and in 1868 Andrew Dunlop was joint tenant in Thornbroke and Dean's Mill.

BAIRD'S MILL

Three miles and a half down the burn from Dean's Mill was Baird's Mill. This mill was situated on a side road about a mile from Crosshill village. The dam was close to the road, and the water was conducted nearly direct on to the waterwheel, which was an iron bucket high breast with from twelve to fourteen feet fall. The lade was long and held a considerable amount of water, and was used partly as a dam after driving the waterwheel. The tailrace ran below the roadway and joined the main burn which discharges into the River Girvan about half a mile further on.

The mill was fitted with three pairs of stones, one pair for shelling, one pair for oatmeal and one pair for cattle provender. The first gear from the water-wheel was a large cast iron level pinion called the pit wheel which meshed into two of the small pinions on the millstone spindles to drive the stones. The shelling stone was belt driven. The mill was fitted for oatmeal milling with dust sieve and shud fanners, meal sieve and meal shud fanners. John McKissock was miller here in 1851, and was still returned as miller in 1868. In the year 1775 Robert and John MacFadzen were in possession of Baird's Mill. This mill was still working in 1946 and was occupied by the owner.

DRUMMOCHREEN [53]

Down the river Girvan from Crosshill about four miles is the estate of Drummochreen, which was a small estate with a mansion house. Abercrombie in his *History of Carrick* gives a description of it which must be very complete. It had everything that an estate should have - cattle, sheep, poultry, game, fishing, coal, moss, meadow and marle with corn mill and waukmill, and was the property of the McAlexanders in 1601 and for a considerable time previously. In a map of 1828, the house was in ruins and the corn mill had disappeared, but the waukmill was still standing. David McAlexander's name appeared in a law case with reference to the mill dam of Drummochreen. This legal action took place between him and Quintin Kennedy in 1664, and resulted in the latter obtained letters of horning[54] against him.

John McAlexander of Drummochreen had his estate confiscated (forfeited) after the Bothwell rising and had some difficulty in recovering it after the Restoration. A list of fugitives published on May 5, 1684, includes John McAlexander, younger, of Drummochreen forfeited; Gilbert German, weaver in Drummochreen; and Hugh Purdie, miller in

Fergussons of Kilkerran.

DAILLY MILL

This mill was situated in the village of Dailly close to the main street. There was a wide grain growing district around Dailly, and also large dairy farms. The roads were good and very convenient with many road junctions in and around the village. A bridge at the end of the street gives access to the north side of the river and to one of the main roads from Girvan to Ayr.

The River Girvan passes a short distance behind where the mill stood and the mill obtained its power from a dam in the river. The dam dyke started from the north bank and crossed in a slope down the river to the intake. It was high and pitched with stones and was still in use in 1947. Two sluices regulated the water into the lade which was about a furlong and a half long and capable of carrying a good volume of water down to the water wheel, which was a breast paddle. After passing the water wheel the water fell into the tailrace and was conducted back into the river. The tailrace had been excavated very deep to furnish the water wheel with as great a fall as possible, and it was carried down the river for a good distance to protect the system from back water in a time of flood.

The mill was three stories and attic in height, large and well built. The machinery was geared off the pit wheel on to a horizontal shaft. There were four pairs of millstones in the mill geared by level pinions off this shaft. One pair was used for shelling oats and also for smutting wheat, one pair for oatmeal, one pair for cattle provender and one pair for flour. The oatmeal plant was the usual sieves, fanners and elevators. The flour mill was fitted with silks - the only mill in Ayrshire south of the river Doon equipped in that way.

No flour was produced at this mill after the late nineteenth century, although it was in good order with strong water-power and up-to-date in machinery. It suffered with the rest of the mills through the tariff being taken off imported flour. About 1880 the mill was let to Messrs. Adam Wilson and Sons to be used as a sawmill in addition to the corn mill, timber products being the principal trade.

When the writer visited the mill on November 7 1946 workmen were taking down the front wall. All that remained of the mill was being carried to fill up the tailrace. The lade was also to be filled in. The mill site and land attached was being levelled and prepared for a public park for Dailly. The full length of the field from the intake to where the tailrace joined the river was about three and a half furlongs.

In 1851 Adam Andrew was miller in Dailly. The last miller was William S. Fettes, who was there for over thirty years. He retired in 1939, when the mill was closed. Mr Fettes died in the same year. The mill was on the estate of Bargany and in the 1840's the Duc de Coigny was proprietor. The proprietor in 1947 was Colonel North Dalrymple Hamilton.

KITTYBEG MILL[55]

On the Lindsayston of Kilkerran Burn about half a mile above Moorston and near Gittybeg farm was Gittybeg or Kittybeg Mill. The burn rises near to Fillyhill and Gallowhill,

On the Lindsayston of Kilkerran Burn about half a mile above Moorston and near Gittybeg farm was Gittybeg or Kittybeg Mill. The burn rises near to Fillyhill and Gallowhill, one feeder from each, and is joined by the Dallamford and Dobbingstone Burns before reaching the Old Castle of Kilkerran at Lindsayston.

There was a dam or small loch for collecting water when the burn was low and another dam close to the mill. Both dams could be shut at night. When the high dam filled it ran over into the bed of the burn continuing on and filling the lower dam so that more water was available for the morning working. This was a fairly common practice at mills with small burns for water-power. The burn continues on past Moorston and discharges its water into the River Girvan above Dailly Mill dam. This was the mill of the old barony and estate of Kilkerran, and all tenants would be thirled to it. Records show that the mill was fuctional in 1828, but no evidence of it existed in 1947. The Fergussons of Kilkerran received a grant of land in Ayrshire in the time of King Robert in Ayrshire.

OLD DAILLY MILL

Continuing down the river from New Dailly for about three and a half miles is the Penwhapple Burn, a tributary of the River Girvan. On this burn a short distance from the mouth was Old Dailly or Camreggan Mill. The burn is large and provided a good supply of water for the mill. It rises among the hills near Whitewaun and running down through the glen past Penkill joins the river below the old church.

In 1947 the lade had been filled up and could not be traced, but the tailrace below the mill could still be seen. The water wheel had been cleared away, but its position could be easily seen on the north gable of the building, where it had left its mark on the stones by grinding a circle on them.

The machinery of the mill had been removed and the second storey of the building converted into a dwelling house, which was occupied in 1947. At the door of the house was lying the freestone eye of a French burr millstone, showing that the mill had at least two pairs of millstones in it. The French burr stones were not used for shelling oats, a Kaimshill or Derby Peak being required, so that a pair of Kaimshill and also a pair of French burr would have been in the mill. Tenant in the mill in 1851 was Andrew Hair, and in 1868 William Andrew was returned as farmer-tenant of the mill and mill lands of Old Dailly or Camreggan Mill.

TROCHRAGUE or BARONS MILL[56]

Above threequarters of a mile below Old Dailly Mill on the north bank of the River Girvan was Trochrig or Trochrague Mill, in the parish of Girvan and on the estate of Trochrig. In 1947 the site formed part of the farm of Robstone.

Robert Boyd of Trochrig was served heir to his father the Archbishop on February 16, 1608, in the ten-pound-land of Trochrig with the mill and the five merk land of Barneile. The Boyds are of the Penkill family, decended from Robert Boyd of Kilmarnock. The estate was acquired by the Fergussons of Kilkerran about the beginning of the nineteenth century, but by

1947 was mostly owned by resident farmers.

A visit to the site revealed only a cottage but very little of the ruins of the mill. Part of the lade and tailrace could be traced, and of the machinery the only part left was the wooden axle of the water wheel with the rings and gudgeons still on it, and also the plummer blocks and bearings. Judging by the space it once occupied, the waterwheel had been about four and a half feet wide, and the mill driven by segment gears. No date was seen when the mill ceased oatmeal production, but it was subscquently a wool and sawmill.

The name was later changed to Barons Mill, and in 1851 James Barons was returned as feuer in Boghead House. Later John Kennedy, wool-miller, and Mrs Thomas Potts and John Potts were all returned for Barons Mill.

BRIDGE MILL

Further down the river, about a mile and a half below and on the same side as Barons Mill, was Bridge Mill close to the shore road and about half a mile from the town of Girvan. The water power was from the river, which carries a large volume here and there was always an ample supply except in very dry seasons.

The water wheel was a large breast paddle about five feet wide and giving from 25 to 30 horse power. The building was four storeys in height which enabled large hoppers to be used. The mill was driven from the pit wheel on the water wheel axle which drove the main vertical shaft of the mill. There were four pairs of stones in the mill, three pairs of which were driven with a crown cog wheel from this shaft. The other pair were driven with overhead bevel pinions on the second floor.

The oatmeal plant had the usual sieves and fanners. When the finished oatmeal was discharged by the rotary meal sieve it fell into a smaller sieve with a tumbler which discharged the meal into the sack at short intervals and kept the meal of even consistency. The kiln was potted and held about a ton of oats. The mill was fitted with a sack tackle used for hauling sacks to the upper floors and drawing the dried corn off the kiln.

Tenants in the mill in 1851 were James and John Austin, millers, and in 1868 Hugh Dickie, farmer and miller. The proprietors and occupiers in 1947 were Hutchison and McCreath, Ltd., grain merchants.

THE RIVER STINCHAR [57]

From the road bridge at Ballantrae the first mill on the river fully a mile up was Aird Mill. After another mile was the water of Tig, which also had a mill. Following the Stinchar again for two miles was the site of Craigneil Mill and in two miles and a half that of Craig Mill. The Stinchar takes a wide sweep here and is joined by the Dusk, which had several mills on it. Inside the bend was Almont Mill, and continuing up the Stinchar for two miles and a half to the Assel burn was the mill of that name. Following the river for about two and a half miles was Pinclanty Mill and about three and a half miles farther on past the village of Barr was Barr Mill.

BARR MILL

This was the first mill on the Stinchar from its source nine or ten miles farther up. The mill was on the estate of Barr on which nearly the whole village was built and the mill was in all probability there before the village. The estate of Barr was the property of David Kennedy in 1629, and the Earl of Cassillis in 1668. In 1681 the proprietor was Thomas McJarrow of Barr. Two of the McJarrows, James and John, were on the list of fugitives in the time of Charles II (1684). Barr Mill like many of the country mills had a small farm attached to it. Before the middle of last century Miller Gourlay was tenant. In 1851 William Burgess, farmer, was tenant.

Kirkdandie Fair

Barr village is on the Gregg burn which joins the Stinchar half a mile from the mill. Passing Alton Albany the next place of note is Kirkdandie where the famous fair was held on the last Saturday in May. It is said that at the beginning of the nineteenth century from fifty to sixty tents were erected on the fair day but by the middle of the century they had dwindled to four or five. This fair was for the sale of every kind of merchandise, most of it arriving on pack saddles. It was also a feeing fair.

PINCLANTY MILL

Following the river down for fully a mile and a half Pinclanty Mill was on south bamk of the Stinchar. Robert Alexander of Corsclays was retoured in the following lands in 1658: the three pound land of Kirkdandie and Ballibeg, the two-merk land of Vicartoun, the forty shilling land of Lommochie, the merk land of Laggangill, the merk land of Drummolong, the two merk land of Corseleys, the forty shilling land of Drummoir, the forty shilling land of Pinmore and Lagansaroch, the two merk land of Cairnquhin, the corn mill of Pinclanty with the salmon fishing in the Stinchar, and the merk land of Pinclanty. This mill was still functioning until early in the twentieth century. Tenant in 1851 was John Carswell and in 1868 Matthew McWhirter. The mill was in the parish of Colmonell.

ASSEL MILL

Situated close to Pinmore Viaduct and about half a mile up from where the Assel burn joins the Stinchar was Assel Mill. It was on the estate of Pinmore, and in the parish of Colmonell. The old corn mill is said to have stood where the saw mill was in the 1940's. The mill was not driven by the Assel burn but by a smaller burn that joined the Assel at the mill site. The advantage was the high fall in this burn - about thirty feet, however only about fifteen feet were employed. The water wheel - an iron bucket overshot - discharged its water directly into the Assel. The dam for the sawmill was close to the road at Kinclear and appeared to be the same dam used for the old meal mill. In 1658 Robert Alexander was proprietor of the sixteen shilling and eight penny land called Nether Milltoun of Assel, and millstead of the same, part of the five merk ten shilling land of McMurristoun or Ballig extending to sixteen shilling and eight penny land of old extent in Glenstinchar within in the earldom of Carrick, and part of the mains of Daljarrock upon the south side of the water of Stinchar. Up till the 1940's only two natives of Scotland had attained the position of Lord Mayor of London, James Shaw of Kilmarnock and Andrew Lusk, who was born at Assel. In 1684 James Ferguson, miller in Assell, was a covenanter who was charged with reset, but did not however appear at the court at Edinburgh. He was on the list of fugitives.

ALMONT MILL [58]

Situated within a quarter of a mile of the iron bridge over the Stinchar at Hollowchapel in the parish of Colmonell was Almont Mill. The nine and a half merk lands of Daljarrock, in which the mill was situated, was divided into the following holdings: the ten shilling lands of Shaward; the ten shilling lands of Netherholm; the thirty shilling lands of Barnhill, Millholm and Craigencrae; the five shilling lands of McCallanston or McAllanstown; the five shilling lands of Alehouse with the mill called Almont Mill; the twenty shilling lands of Grassard; the ten shilling lands of Balcacherie, and the half merk land of Baiker.

The mill dam was nearly half a mile below Daljarrock House and crossed the river roughly from south to north at an angle to the intake at the sluice which regulated the water into the lade and conducted it to the top of the wheel which was about fourteen feet in diameter. A wooden trows or trough with a hatch was used, the hatch being to bypass the water that was not required. The wheel was breasted and had also shallow buckets. After passing the mill the lade continued for a considerable distance before joining the river.

Previous to 1892 the mill was fitted with a flour plant, but as little or no wheat was grown in the district it was removed to make more floor space. A barley mill was also included in the plant.

Mill Machinery

The mill had three floors. Hoppers were all filled from the top one, and the kiln was also loaded from there. The drive from the waterwheel was by a heavy pit wheel geared into a small pinion on the main vertical shaft of the mill. On this shaft was keyed a large cog crown wheel which meshed into three small pinions on the spindles of the stones.

The mill was fitted with three pairs of millstones - one pair French burrs for oatmeal, one pair Derby peak for shelling oats, and one pair edge built French burrs for cattle provender. The edge built stones were considered the best for provender up to the time Joseph Trapp, an Austrian, invented the "ever sharp" in the 1900's.

The spindles and running stones were carried with wooden bridges, hinged at the one end and hung on an iron rod with a screw at the other for raising and lowering the running stone for the different grades of material being ground. The bed stones were laid on the second floor of the mill inside cast iron cribs around the main vertical shaft and placed to fit the gears below. The spindles projected up through the eye of the bed stone. A small shaft with a box coupling was fitted on the end of the spindles to drive the tickler or clap which regulated the grain into the eye of the stone.

The oatmeal and shelling stones were carried by three-toed rhinds which were bedded in the stones. The provender stone had a universal balance rhind which was not suitable for oatmeal or shelling. The main vertical shaft continued up through the third floor nearly to the roof, where was the drive for the sack tackle which was of the fixed and slack pulley type. All elevators were driven from this floor.

Making of Oatmeal

To make oatmeal the oats were first put over a cockle sieve from which they fell into the shelling hopper. Passing through the stones they were elevated to the dust rotary sieve, then passed through the large fanners which separated the groats from the husks or shuds. The groats were again elevated to the hopper of the meal stones and passed on through and were discharged into the rotary meal sieve in which there were three perforated sheets for dressing of the meal - Nos. 9, 10 and 11. The overflow from No. 9 fell into a set of small fanners which blew out the meal shud. The round meal was again put through the stones and passed into the meal sieve along with the overflow from Nos. 10 and 11. The material passing through No. 11 was the finished meal.

The kiln was small, being well loaded with a ton of oats. The plates on it were fourteen inches square with round holes, but the furnace drew well, which is one of the main qualities of a kiln. The machinery of the mill was supplied and erected by J. & T. Young, Vulcan Foundry, Newton Green, Ayr.

A Famous Name

The name Almont probably derived from the old hill close beside the mill. A monument was erected at the top of the hill to the memory of John Snell of Oxford bursary fame. The hill was known as the shelling hill and was used for winnowing the shelled oats until 1710 when Meikle imported from Holland the first set of fanners to be used in Scotland. Up till this time all mills had a shelling hill. A family of the name of Carnochan was in Almont Mill about then. There were several of this family in the parish, who were millers and millwrights. When Meikle imported the fanners the local minister preached a sermon on the sin of using artificial wind when God's wind was already provided for their use.

In 1892 the site of Andrew Snell's house and smithy was indicated as at Almont Mill road-end in a small field on the lade side, but research by the late Dr. Milroy and others found it to be the old thatch cottage called Ladeside, which was about a hundred and fifty yards from the mill roadend. There lived Andrew Snell the smith and his wife, Margaret Carnochan, the father and mother of John Snell who assisted so many Scottish students through Oxford University.

One day in the summer of 1892 a carriage and pair drove up to the mill door. A gentleman alighted, stepped on to the mill platform and introduced himself to the miller. "My name is Lusk, I am a nephew of ex-Lord Mayor Lusk of London," he said. "My father had this mill and Almont farm thirty-five years ago when the mill was burned. May I have a look round the mill?" He explained to the miller that he was a rancher from the USA. In 1851 Adam Calderwood was miller in Almont and Andrew Lusk was farmer.

Breach In The Dam

In the year 1893 - a large tree was blown down at Pinmore House. Some time later following heavy rain the Stinchar rose in flood and through the night it washed the tree into the river. The tree was several tons in weight, and when it travelled round the bend at Daljarrock Bridge it had a straight run for the dam of nearly a quarter of a mile. The river travels fast here, and the tree struck the dam in the middle carrying away sixty-four feet of the beams lining and pitching, and finished up stranded on a gravel bank below the dam.

To repair the dam trees had to be cut and beams sawn and all wood needed for the work prepared. On the last day of the year a skeleton dam was finished and the water began to rise, but it never got to its potential height. With the weight of the water the stays reared up and with a crash the whole of the woodwork was transported down the river. Subsequently, iron permanent rails were employed with supporting fish plates bolted to the beams resulting in a more secure fixture which held for over twenty years. Thereafter a further breach occurred at the same spot bending the iron rails. The Stinchar had won again.

After the destruction of the dam and closing of the mill the machinery was sold to D.H. & F. Reid, engineers, Ayr, who in turn sold part of it to the second Lord Kitchener for a mill he was erecting on his estate in Kenya for the grinding of mealies for his workers. He evidently had a waterfall on the estate as a water turbine was also exported there.

Daljarrock estate was possessed for many generations by the Kennedys. According to Dr. Ross a daughter of Robert Kennedy, Margaret Kennedy, born November 3, 1766 and died February 1795, was the heroine of Burns' song *Young Peggy Blooms*. She was a niece of Gavin Hamilton of Mauchline.

According to Abercrombie the house stood at the head of a pleasant plain called Daljarrock holm, and included all the land from the road to the river down to the mill lade. In 1892 it was cultivated by Robert Hodge, who was tenant in Almont farm and also had the corn and sawmills there.

CRAIG MILL[59]

Passing down the river from Almont Mill dam and round the head where the Dusk joins the Stinchar - a distance of about two miles - there is a burn on the north bank which falls into the river just below Poundland or Pinlan. It was on this burn that the building called Craig Mill once stood, about a quarter of a mile above Craig House. The mill, which was a small one with one pair of stones, was swept away by the scour of the burn, which comes very rapidly down from the hills. Nothing was left of the mill but a few stones in 1947.

There was a good fall on the burn and the dam would not require to be far up to achieve a sufficient head of water for the breast wheel. The mill stood about forty yards from the public road and was driven by this burn which divided the lands of Craig from those of Pinlan.

Andrew Kennedy, cartwright; Miss Shearer, grocer, and James Howie, currier (a dresser of tanned leather) in Craig Mill. A field on the higher side of the road was called the mill or the miller's field.

The estate of Craig belonged to the Grahams in 1601, and was acquired by Kennedy of Kirkhill in 1616 and by a branch of the Fergussons in 1667. From them it passed to a family of the name of Hutchison, and again came into the Kennedy family, who sold it to Mrs Mitchell who was the propietor in 1947. In 1851 the tenant in Craig House was Benjamin Hall and at Pinlan was a school and Reformed Presbyterian Church of which the Rev. R. Harkness was minister.

CRAIGNEIL MILL[60]

Following the river for two and three quarter miles was the site of the dam for Craigneil Mill. From the intake to the mill was a quarter of a mile, it being built in a curve of the river which gave the lade a straight run from the intake to the end of the tailrace. Access was by a road from Colmonell to Glen Tig below which the lade ran to the mill.

According to a plan of 1828 the mill was built about a furlong from the south bank of the river. The water wheel was breast and a large volume of water was available. The number of pairs of stones in the mill was not ascertained but in all probability there were two. It was the barony mill of Craigneil and at one time a large part of the estate was thirled to it. The old ruined castle was half a mile from the mill, and had walls six feet thick. It stood on the top of a limestone rock opposite the village. A quarry, started below it, was worked too near the old building, and local legend relates that whilst attending service in the church one Sunday the congregation heard a loud rumbling noise. At the conclusion of the service they found that part of the castle had fallen into the quarry below.

Craigneil is said to have been built in the thirteenth century by Neil, Earl of Carrick, hence its designation. The castle, which commanded a fine view of the Stinchar valley, being a part of the earldom of Carrick, was sometimes occupied by King Robert Bruce during the war of independence. It was later possessed by the Kennedys of Cassillis. The mill was closed in the latter half of the nineteenth century, David Findlay being returned miller in 1851.

GLENTIG MILL[61]

Continuing along the valley of the River Stinchar for two-and-a-half miles is the Tig water on which, at a place called Glentig, was a mill, which is mentioned in an old charter: *The ten merk land of Glentig with the corn mill of the same, the five merk land and half merk land of Meakill Sallauchane and the four merk land of Little Sallauchane in propertie and tenandrie, with the pertinentis lying in the earldom of Carrick, etc. to David Kerr as attorney for Matthew Dunduff alias (Stewart) of that ilk after the form and tenour of the said precept past upon one retour make before the Sheriff of Ayr and his deputy to that effect,* dated May 5 1586.

From the date of the mill it was likely to be another of the small mills with one pair of *past upon one retour make before the Sheriff of Ayr and his deputy to that effect,* dated May 5 1586.

From the date of the mill it was likely to be another of the small mills with one pair of stones and geared by cog and rung. The water power was from the Tig rivulet which rises at Craignaburrie Hill in the parish of Ballantrae, runs two miles north-east to the boundary of the parish of Colmonell, and from there it divides the two parishes on to its junction with the Stinchar, passing in its course the farms of Glenour, Shalloch-on-Tig, Bellymore, Auchenflower, Glentig and Mains of Tig. There was a ford on the rivulet called Heron's ford. Latterly it was bridged over, but the name was retained for the clachan.

In 1802 the tenants in Mains of Tig were James Graham, a brother of Douglas Graham, the immortal *Tam O'Shanter*, and his wife, Janet McQueiston. The old kirk of Kirkcudbright Innertig stood here, but when the new kirk was built at Ballantrae in 1604 the old one eventually became a ruin. In 1851 John McClure was blacksmith and farmer at Heronsford and David Coulter was wright there. The proprietor was Andrew Farquhar Gray of Glentig.

AIRD MILL[62]

Returning to the river again at the junction of the Tig, a map of 1828 showed five isles in the bed of the Stinchar apart from the delta at the mouth. The first is about three furlongs below the confluence of the Tig and is called the Isle of Pins. On the opposite side was the intake of the lade for Aird Mill which ran for three quarters of a mile before it reached the mill, and having passed the water wheel the tail race joined the river fully a quarter of a mile farther down. This was the barony mill of Ardstinchar a large estate possessed by one of the main branches of the Kennedys, that of Bargany Kennedys, for a period of 250 years.

The mill was driven by a breast wheel and was situated between the road and the river a mile from the bridge at Ballantrae. A large part of the barony was thirled to the mill and an ample supply of water was available so that if the mill was well equipped with machinery it would be capable of a good output of meal.

The Stinchar valley was well cultivated and the corn grown there was of good quality. It is worthy of note that farm rents back in the seventeenth century were paid in kind. One of them reads thus: *7 bolls 2 furlots once shelled meal, 2 bolls twice shelled meal and 4 bolls beer at Yule and Candlemas.* A boll of meal was approximately 63.5 kg, and a furlot or firlot was a quarter of a boll. In the 1940's the corn was mostly twice shelled unless there was a brush machine or some other machine to assist the shelling stones. The lands of the barony of Ardstinchar were dispersed in 1816 and sold in lots by Sir Hew Dalrymple who succeeded to the estate in 1796.

ON THE DUSK[63]

Starting at the confluence of the Stinchar and the Dusk, one of its tributaries, and following the river up past Pinwherry for about a mile and a quarter is the Water of Muck, a large burn with no indication or record of a mill ever being on it. Two miles farther up, there joins the Dusk the burn from the mill loch on which Glenwhask Mill was situated, and close above was Kildonan Mill. Following the river again to within half a mile of the meeting house and on the north bank of the river close to Barrhill, there is marked on the 1828 plan another mill. Two miles beyond it was Lochton Mill, and in fully a quarter of a mile was Dusk Loch where several of the feeders of the river join. Chirmory and Craigens burns coming from near the boundary of Wigtownshire join before reaching the loch. The burn from Arnsheen and Drumlamford lochs and another small burn join in near the loch. This forms the head waters of the Dusk.

At Lochton Mill the dam was some distance above the mill. The water was conducted by a lade down to the top of the mill wheel, which was an iron bucket type with the water turning on the top and driving by the breast. It was out of use before 1947 owing to a breach in the dam. An oil engine was being used for crushing oats only. The mill was three storeys in height with three floors and three pairs of stones and was of strong construction with cast iron columns and bridges. Driven by heavy gears on the main verticle shaft of the mill the stones were turned by a crown cog wheel. The whole fittings of the mill were of the type supplied by Messrs. J. and T. Young, Vulcan Foundry, Newton-on-Ayr, and were probably erected by that firm about the middle of the nineteenth century. The kiln was of medium size and was loaded from the top floor. The mill was on the estate of Drumlamford and in the Arnsheen division of Colmonell. In the middle of the nineteenth century the tenant was William Dongan, farmer and miller.

Following the Dusk[64] from Lochton Mill was a waulk-mill built by Hugh Galt about 1880. No corn mill existed here. Continuing down the river the site of another mill is reached below the farm of Balluskie, which is the mill Hugh Galt was in before removing up the river to the waulk mill. He was returned in the Directory of Ayrshire of 1851 as farmer and miller, and William Galt as *farmer, Waulk Mill, Barrhill.* In all probability there was a corn mill there at an early date. Some of these mills were let with a condition that meal milling could be carried on along with other milling. This mill was driven from the Dusk and was on Kildonan Estate, the property of Dr. Hamilton about the year 1835.

About a quarter of a mile down the river was a saw mill driven from a small burn coming off the high ground and augmented by the water from the Mill Loch. It had an iron bucket wheel, the water being conducted on to the top of the wheel. The drive was by the breast. The building was old and appeared to have been used for some other purpose before it became a saw mill. There was evidence of modification to the old building to accomodate the gears for the sawmill.

A short distance down the river it is joined by the Mill Loch Burn. This burn rises in the parish of Barr at a place called March Loch, although there is no loch shown on the map. Running south through the Mill Loch it reaches the mill dam of what is locally known as Glenwhask, but is marked on the map as Kildonan. In 1851 John Sloan was miller in Glenwhask. This was the last of the mills on the Stinchar and Dusk, ten in number, with only one of them working in 1947, producing bruised oats. Many of them had completely disappeared by this date.

ON CARRICK SHORE [65]

BALLOCHDOWAN MILL

Leaving the Ballantrae and Stranraer road where Killantringan Toll stood, and turning to the west, past the house of that name was a small clachan where there was a school, a schoolhouse and a smithy with a mill about a furlong further down called Ballochdowan. The driving power for this mill was from the Currarie Burn, which rises on Benelowan hill and turning towards the west runs for a considerable distance in a deep glen before it reaches where the mill stood, passing on and entering the sea at Port Currarie, a distance of a mile and three quarters from the mill site. The burn is small and does not carry a large volume of water, but the mill was built at a high waterfall. The writer believed that nearly thirty feet of fall could be realised, half of which would be ample for the work required. A turbine water wheel would have given good results here. A ten inch turbine with about 400 cubic foot of water per minute would develop about 30 horse power. There was a suitable place for a retaining dam a short distance above the mill but none of the local people remembered such a dam being used although for a small burn like this it is necessary to have one to collect water in a dry time.

In 1947 the mill was overgrown with brushwood and could not be easily seen. It had been built close to the bank of the burn, which was very high requiring much masonry support. The building was strongly constructed as much of it was still standing at that time. The top flat was on a level with the road and there the corn had been taken in to be dried. The entrance road had been fairly level and well made. Looking down from the top the building was roofless and no machinery could be seen: all had been removed.

In the middle of the nineteenth century it must have been an interesting old mill. At that time Anthony McLelland was miller. In 1868 Bernard Murphy was returned as miller and tenant of the lands, etc., of Miller's Croft. In 1816 Sir Hugh Hamilton dispersed the barony lands of Ardstinchar and sold it in lots along with other lands. Lot 10, then called Ballendowan, was sold to James Johnston who was Comptroller of Customs at Ayr. It was on the estate of Glenapp in 1947.

COLING MILL [66]

The road from Ballochdownan to Coling Mill, a distance of over two miles, approaches near to the farm of Bigpark. In 1851 - no fewer that six farmers were returned as farming there - William Agnew, Alexander Barclay, Peter Gibb, Samuel Moors, John McDowall and John Ross. Nearby Downan, or Downanpark as it was sometimes called, was tenanted by Robert Wright, at that time the property of Lord Orkney of Glen App Lodge.

Coling Mill was situated about a mile from the bridge at Ballantrae, close to the public road, and in a picturesque setting. It was driven by a burn that rises at Smyrton Hill and runs northwest past Smyrton farm to reach the site of the mill. Further on the burn enters the sea at the mouth of the Stinchar. The dam was above the mill and the water was conducted in a lade and trows down to the water wheel sixteen feet in diameter by four feet wide, with large buckets capable of carrying a heavy weight of water which came on to the wheel at the breast about two feet below the top. The water wheel was all iron and well built.

The drive to the gears was from the axle, by a large bevel pinion, which meshed into a small pinion on the main vertical shaft of the mill. A large crown cog wheel was keyed to it meshing into the three pinions on the spindles of the stones of which there were three pairs round the crown wheel, one pair each for shelling, oatmeal and cattle provender.

The oatmeal mill had the usual fittings - sieves, fanners and elevators. The sack tackle was of the clutch type. The kiln was small - fifteen feet square - taking a hundred eighteen inches square cast iron plates to cover it. The plates were modern.. The kiln building was potted, with the furnace opening on the floor of the mill which was three storeys in height. The millstones were lifted by a jack from the floor above them. In 1851 Allan Davie was returned as miller and farmer in Coling Mill.

CUNDRY MILL[67]

Cundry Mill was situated on the Lendal Water about a mile and a quarter from the bridge at Lendalfoot. The Lendal, which provided the driving power of the mill, rises in the parish of Girvan near Lochtown and Soapstone rock. After flowing through a small loch near the farm of Knocklach it enters the parish of Colmonell, passing the farms of Currarie, Millenderdale, Cundry Mains and Burchlewan to reach the mill. About a quarter of a mile up the Lendal was the weir for conducting the water from the rivulet into the lade which carried it down to a retaining dam above the mill and, after passing the mill, the tailrace joined the Lendal again close above the road bridge.

The mill was on the north bank of the rivulet and the road in was a short distance above the upper end of the bridge. The buildings were in ruins in the 1940's. The fall on the waterwheel could not be ascertained, but it would be high as it is a broiling rivulet when in spate. Its bed is full of boulders and rock.

There may also have been a mill at Millenderdale but no record has been found. Cundry Mill was on the estate of Knockdaw, and in the year 1632 Catharina Kennedy, heiress to the late David Kennedy, of Knockdaw, was retoured in the superiority and lands of Cundry, which included the mill. David was succeeded by John Kennedy, of Knockdaw, whose son, David Kennedy was retoured in the lands of Cundry, Knockdaw and others in 1650. Sometime after that these lands were acquired by Kennedy of Bargany who held them for a considerable time; and in 1947 they were the property of Mrs Mitchell of Dalreoch, Colmonell. In 1851 James Barclay was miller in Cundry Mill.

SHALLOCH MILL[68]

Shalloch Mill was situated on the Girvan to Ballantrae road about a mile from the town of Girvan. It was driven from a burn that rises about a mile above Pinminnoch, and passing the farm of that name is joined by several small burns. The farm of Pinminnoch was farmed in the middle of the nineteenth century by John Earl and on it there were four portioners, Grace, Ann, Jean and Mary Earl.

The burn continues on down the glen at the base of the Bynehill and it is augmented by many other burns until it reached the weir which was about a quarter of a mile from the mill. Here was the intake for the retaining dam. A long lade carried the water below a road down into the dam and at the other end was a sluice to regulate the water into another short lade for driving the waterwheel. The tailrace passed on through below the roadway direct to the sea. The burn itself discharges its water into the sea about a furlong further to the south. The mill had been closed for a number of years but the old iron water wheel was still in place in 1947. The buildings were being used for other purposes.

One of the millers used to say that he kept a company of navvies for cleaning his dam, but they were winged navvies - ducks. They kept stirring up the mud in the retaining dam and when the mill was working the tailrace discharged the water and mud direct into the sea.

About a mile to the south was Ardmillan House and estate, possessed by the Crawfords. Abercummie describes it as a palace surrounded by a deep broad ditch, strengthened with a moveable bridge at the entry able to secure the owner from a sudden attack of the wild people of this locality. To enable him to endure a siege he was provided with a well in his court and a hand mill in the house for grinding meal or malt with which two men set to work could grind a firlot (35 lb) of oatmeal in the space of an hour. The last family occupying Shalloch Mill was McMillan. David Thomson was miller here in the 1850's.

GIRVAN MILL[69]

According to William Johnston's plan Girvan Mill was situated close to the town and at the north corner of the public park on the south side of the Bank Burn near the footbridge. The mill was cleared away by 1947 and nothing of it was left to tell where it stood, but some of the garden walls nearby had been built with old building stones which may have been from the mill. About a furlong to the east of the mill was Balloch cottage where in the year 1850 resided John Wilson who was factor for Bargany estate.

The Bank Burn was the driving power of the mill: sometimes it was call the Mill Burn. It rises near Laggan Hill and, running through a small loch of that name towards the north west, it is joined in about threequarters of a mile by a feeder from near Trowier hill. The burn then passes Coalpots and continues nearly a mile farther on to where the mill stood. After passing the mill the tailrace joined the burn below the footbridge and carried on down through the Flushes and discharged its waters into the upper end of the harbour at the mouth of the River Girvan.

The mill was driven by a breast paddle waterwheel. All the ground was levelled to accomodate the Public Park, and little information was available about the dams, the lade and bypass. At an early date the Bank Burn alone provided the driving power of the mill. Many of the country mills up to eighteenth century functioned only to grind oatmeal. The sifting and other work was done by hand, so that when the extra machinery was put in to do that work it required more power. It may have been then that the Doune burn was made use of by opening a lade between it and the Bank Burn.

Ballochtoul Castle stood within a quarter of a mile of Girvan Mill and in Johnston's map of 1828 it is described as in ruins. It passed through several owners and was finally acquired by the Bargany estate and the site cleared.

LADYBURN MILL[70]

According to Johnstone's map Ladyburn Mill was situated a quarter of a mile from the main road from Girvan to Maybole. The plan map shows a short road turning in at the north of Dunnymuck and ending at the mill. The modern map shows the road extended up the hollow, there joining the old road to Girvan near Ladybank House possessed by Mr Nisbet in 1830.

The burn which was the water power of the mill was the one rising above McGowanston and continuing down to Ladybank House where the plan shows the intake of the lade leaving the burn, passing below the old Girvan road and continuing on down for half a mile to reach where the retaining dam was sited above the mill. From there the water was regulated to the mill water wheel which discharged its water into a tailrace and joined the Lady Burn, which is the larger of two burns, and also the longest. According to the old map it rises at Gilshacking and running towards the west passes Auchensaw, South Thrave, Drumuck, Braehead and High Dunnymuck, then past the mill and enters the sea near the Dipple.

After closing as a meal mill it was converted into a barn and the water wheel used for driving a threshing mill. Some mills included a threshing mill in their plant and did the threshing for the small farms around. Little can be said about the interior of the mill as all the machinery was cleared away, also the buildings. The mill was in the parish of Kirkoswald and in the 1840's Ladybank was the property of Charles Boyd.

BALLOCHNEIL MILL[71]

Ballochneil Mill was situated on the Maybole-Girvan road a mile and a quarter south of Kirkoswald. It was driven by the Milton Burn, which rises in two lochs both in Kirkoswald parish - Mochrum and Craigdow. The burn first runs south between the farms of Glenluie and Mosside, turning west on passing under the road bridge. It continues on to near Kirkoswald and is joined there by the burn from Craigdow Loch. Passing Corrieston and Minnybae with Croftingee, near the old road to Girvan it comes down to the head of the milldam and in a quarter of a mile to the site of the old mill. Three-quarters of a mile farther on it comes to the site of Culzean Mill dam and then past High and Low Drumdow, Culzean Mill and Old Stepend. At the bridge over the Maybole road it is joined by the Maidens road at Milton Cottages. Continuing on through the bents the burn enters the sea at Turnberry Bay.

Ballochneil Mill stood on the opposite side of Milton Burn from High Dalwhat. There was also a farm of Ballochneil and situated there was a ford through to the mill. The weir was about a quarter of a mile up the burn with a lade down to the retaining dam which could not be traced in 1947. From there a short lade conducted the water to the wheel which was a breast paddle. Only one pair of stones is said to have been in the mill, and they were driven by a bevel pit wheel on to the spindle of the stone. The Milton burn is supplemented here by a very strong spring the water from which is collected in a tank and supplied to several of the farms. David Ferguson is understood to have been the last full-time miller here.

What makes this farm and mill famous is the fact that the poet Robert Burns resided here when attending school at Kirkoswald, his father having sent him there to study under Hugh Rodger who was considered a talented teacher. An uncle of Burns, Samuel Brown, brother of the poet's mother, had his home at Ballochneil and here Burns slept in the garret of the farmhouse along with John Niven, the farmer's son. Burns was only three months at Kirkoswald school but a number of the characters in his works are taken from this district, Douglas Graham *(Tam O' Shanter)* being the principal. Graham was the tenant of Laigh Park about a quarter of a mile from Ballochneil.

CULZEAN MILL[72]

This mill was situated about a quarter of a mile from the Girvan and Maybole road and on a road that runs from Milton to the old Girvan road. It was three miles and a half from Culzean Castle and was the property of the Marquis of Ailsa. The weir was on the Milton burn threequarters of a mile above the mill. From there the lade carried the water down to the retaining dam at the mill, then passing below the road, the water was conducted to the top of the water wheel. There it turned and drove down the breast, only a part of the fall being used.

The water wheel was an iron bucket and was still in place in 1947. It had an axle of wood with cast iron gudgeons in each end to run in the bearings. This axle also carried a large pit wheel which meshed into a small bevel pinion on the main vertical shaft of the mill. On this shaft was keyed a large crown cog wheel which meshed into the small pinions on the stone spindles.

The mill was two stories in height and had two pairs of millstones, both pairs of Kaimshill stone. There was also a rotary meal sieve with dust sieve fanners and all the usual equipment. The buildings of the mill were still standing in 1947, and were used for a time as a joiner's shop.

Two of Burns' characters in *Hallowe'en* served in Culzean Mill before they were married - Rab McGraen and Eppie Sim. In 1851 William Renny was miller, and in 1868 James Dinning. The mill was closed in 1900, John Wilson being the last miller.

In the winter of 1882 a Norwegian ship was making its way up the Firth of Clyde to Greenock in very rough weather, the storm ever increasing,. The ship became unmanageable and was driven towards the Ayrshire coast near Turnberry. Missing the rocks by a short distance she was driven into the sandy bay at the foot of the Milton burn. Here the seamen all managed to scramble to the shore and made inland. Coming to Milton Cottages on the Girvan road they tried to rouse the occupants, but they, thinking that it was a company of Maidens fishermen who had been celebrating in Girvan, kept their doors bolted and the sailors turned up the road leading to the old Girvan road.

In a short distance they came to Culzean Mill and there roused the miller and his wife. When he opened the door he found a crowd of jabbering foreign seamen in front of him. None but the captain could speak English but they could all cry "Ship ashore." The miller opened his door and led them into the kitchen. The men all wet and cold would have rushed to the fire, but the captain herded them back. The kitchen got too full for working in, but the miller remembered the large anthracite fire of the kiln and led them down the steep bank to the kiln loggie where they proceeded to dry their wet clothes. A messenger was despatched to Girvan for assistance and in the early morning conveyances were sent out for them. The ship had a very valuable cargo of olive oil which was all salved and after taking weight off the ship it was refloated.

GLENFOOT MILL[73]

Glenfoot Mill was situated in the Maidens village about a furlong up from the bridge on the main road where it turns for the shore road to Girvan. It was driven by a burn which rises above Kirkoswald and running towards the west passes near Glenfoot and Jameston and reaches the site of the mill as marked on Johnston's map of 1828 a little below the bridge that carries the road over the burn to the present roads and runways of the old aerodrome. None of the old buildings of the mill could be seen in 1947. Entrance to it was from the main road.

Within a furlong of the mill on the south side of the burn was Douglaston where Douglas Graham *(Tam O'Shanter)* was born and three furlongs to the south-east was Shanter where he farmed and in all likelihood he and his father before him got some of their corn milled at Glenfoot Mill. At that time there were no rotary sieves in country mills. The corn had to be dried, cooled and shelled. The notice was sent to the farmer to send a man to sift the meal on the day it was to be made. When the melder, which was the quantity of one farmer's corn sent to the mill to be ground at one time, was finished the farmer treated the miller and his helpers to yill (ale) mixed with new meal.

When Johnston compiled his map there were few houses in the Maidens, and none between the burn and the road. On the opposite side was Cellars and three furlongs from the corner along the shore road towards Ardlochan was the smithy. Turning on to the Girvan road was to the road leading to the pier. Here a short distance in is Weary Neuk which John McCarney includes in his song *Girvan fair:*

> Oh there were folk frae Ballantrae
> And some frae far Stranraer, sir
> Frae Minnibole and Colmonell
> Kirkoswald and the Barr, sir
> Frae Weary Neuk and Dinnimuck
> An a' along the shore, sir
> And sic a crowd in Grivan toon
> Was never seen before, sir

South westwards of the mill is an extensive plain mentioned by Sir Walter Scott in his *Lord of the Isles*, where he depicts Bruce's attack on Turnberry Castle:

They gained the chase a wide domain
Left for the Castle's sylvan reign
Seek not the scene the axe the plough
The boor's dull fence have marred it now.

One summer just after 1800 there was a long time of dry hot weather which was followed by a great storm. Much of this land was in potatoes. The storm lifted the dry sand and swept it over the crop. The potatoes were never harvested.

ARDLOCHAN MILL[74]

Near the shore about three quarters of a mile north from the corner of the road at the Maidens and the same distance from Morriston was Ardlochan Mill on the farm of the same name. The water power was derived from a retaining dam in the field above the mill, which was filled in and cultivated along with the rest of the field, but could still be traced in 1947. The lade was covered over to near the water wheel, which was the breast type.

The mill was two storeys in height. The walls were all standing in 1947, but the working part was without the roof. This mill appeared to be of the broken-loft construction, that is, the stones were on a platform about three feet lower than the loft to allow of the hoppers being filled from the floor.

The machinery was all cleared out. The millstones were collected many years ago along with others to be used as seats on the grounds of Culzean Castle. Some of the wood beams for carrying the shafting and the half of the second floor were still in the mill. After the mill stopped grinding oatmeal it was converted into a hone mill but as the water was scarce there would not be sufficient power for this production. The site of the mill lade was still identifiable in 1947.

The bypass and the tail race water entered the sea a short distance from the farmhouse. Near the mill was Hoggstone, tenanted by John McTaggart, whose daughter Helen, became the wife of Douglas Graham *(Tam O'Shanter)* referred to in the poem as Kate:

In vain thy Kate awaits thy comin',
Kate soon will be a woeful woman.

The miller here was Hugh Brown, son of William Brown, Jameston, tenant of Ardlochan or Damhouse of Ardloch near by. Not far from the mill was the change-house where Willie Boden from Burns' poem had his signboard and about which Kate upbraids Tam on the lines:

That ilka melder wi' the miller
Thou sat as lang as thou had siller.

Douglas Graham is reputed to have said of *Tam O'Shanter* that "it was a parcel of lees for he never owned a grey mare or ane ca'd Meg or ony kind o' beast without the tail".

THOMASTON MILL[75]

Thomaston mill was situated about threequarters of a mile west of the old castle of that name and half a mile from the Maybole and Maidens road. The retaining dam was close above the mill, the water being collected there from two burns. One rose near High Thomaston and the other near the old castle. The mill sluice was on the side of an accommodation road which passed the mill and a short lead conveyed the water to the wheel.

No meal was made here after 1850, the mill being converted previous to that time into a sawmill. Near here on an old plan is marked Swinston gate and up above the mill was a row of cottages called Sunnyside. The mill building was in good order in 1947 and appeared to have been renewed and extended since the days of the old mill. The water after passing the wheel, continues down the glen passing near Hogston gate and entering the sea opposite the Keun Rock.

Thomaston mill is famous as the birthplace of Hugh Rodger, son of John Rodger who was miller there. Hugh became schoolmaster at Kirkoswald and the teacher to whom Burns was sent by his father. There were at one time in the parish of Kirkoswald no fewer than seven corn mills in working order, but all were at a standstill by 1947, and many had been cleared away, the last to close being Culzean about the beginning of the twentieth century.

It has been said that Robert Bruce was born in Thomaston castle, that his father and mother having married without the consent of Alexander the king - she being a ward of the Crown - they were expelled from the castle of Turnberry. but a fine was imposed and this settled the matter and they returned.

Tradition ascribes the building of the present old castle to Thomas, third son of Edward Bruce, who became Earl of Carrick, on the death of his brother Alexander. The erection of the castle is dated 1335. The next family in possession of Thomston was the Corries of Kelwood, who held it for many generations. From them it passed to the McIlvanes of Grimmer, and finally to the Kennedy of Culzean. The tenant in 1851 was William Young, farmer and sawmiller, Thomaston, and in 1868 William McFadzean, farmer, Thomaston and Belvaird.

DUNURE MILL[76]

Dunure Mill was situated on the shore road from Ayr to the Maidens about seven miles from Ayr. The water power was from a burn rising on Brown Carrick Hill, which runs towards the west past Dunure Mains and the mill, and enters the sea half a mile south of Port Shuchin. The retaining dam was close above the mill and although not large was deep and could hold a considerable quantity of water. Another waterwheel was in use a short distance above the road bridge for driving a thrashing mill at the farm. Another dam would be required further up the burn above the bridge and ran into the retaining dam of the corn mill so there was no loss of water with the running of the two wheels.

The mill is well built, wide and commodious and three stories in height. The gables are crow-stepped, with a cross on the top of each. The windows are near the gothic, and give the building a churchlike appearance so that it might be said you could make either a kirk or a mill of it. The machinery was all cleared out of the building before 1948, including the waterwheel and the millstones which were used for decorative purposes in front of the farm house of Dunure Mains. There appeared to have been three pairs of stones in the mill, one pair each for shelling, for finishing oat meal and for flour and provender. The kiln was built from the east gable of the mill and was of medium size, potted and had been leaded from the top flat.

This was the barony mill of Dunure to which all the farms on the estate were thirled. The castle is about a mile to the north-west on the rocky shore near the village and port. Near the mouth of the harbour is a conical mount on which the flagstaff was erected. It is called Port Rorie.

Dunure was the early residence and stronghold of the main branch of the Kennedys in Carrick until Sir John Kennedy acquired the barony of Cassillis and took up residence in that house. Dunure was maintained for a considerable time afterwards being the strongest and most secure house against attack. Part of it was destroyed by fire, and the building is now a ruin.

Tenant in the mill previous to 1840 was James Dow, but at that date he removed to Alloway Mill on the Doon. James was also a poet and no less than six of his compositions are included in Finlayson's *Anthology of Carrick*. In 1851 John Crawford was miller.

MONKLAND MILL[77]

Monkland Mill was situated near the Heads of Ayr on a burn of the same name, which rises on Brown Carrick hill, and running towards the north-west past the farms of Carwinshoch, Genoch, Low Glenayes and Largs enters the firth near the old farm house of Bowerhill.

The mill was about a quarter of a mile up the burn and near the monastery to which it belonged, which was suppressed at the Reformation. The mill was functional for a considerable time afterwards. The burn has a good fall and there was a small retaining dam a short distance up. Much of the banks had been washed away by 1948 and the lade was difficult to trace. The waterwheel in use was a breast paddle which in a burn with a fall like this would give a high speed and save wear on the gears.

Up to time of the Reformation the mill would be worked by the monks. The place where the monastery and mill stood was overgrown and the site was indistinguishable. The building stones were removed for use at the farms on the estate.

The entrance road was from the main road near Lagg and passed the mill and monastery to come out at the old farm of Bowerhill. The road was a mile long and curved slightly towards the sea. To the west is Port of Lagg, a natural haven used by light craft as a shelter in stormy weather. Here the fishing boats could run into the sandy beach and wait until the turn of the tide to refloat them. Light cargoes were also landed here.

DUNDUFF MILL

The earliest notice of Dunduff estate in history is in a charter to the Monastery of Melrose, where there is a grant of land to the monks in the reign of William the Lion. In 1558 it was in the possession of William Stewart or Dunduff as the family were sometimes called in the charters. On May 8, 1681 - Nicolas Shearer, Sheriff Depute of Ayr, by virtue of a precept dated March 7 1581, gave sasine of all and whole of the twelve merk lands of Dunduff with the corn mill thereof lying within the earldom of Carrick, &c., to David Kerr acting attorney for Mathew Dunduff (alias Stewart).

This mill was driven by one of the burns rising to the south of Brown Carrick hill and running towards the west reaches the sea between Dunure and Port Lagg. There is no evidence of the location of the mill. The mill was very small and had only one pair of stones and the old cog and rung gears. The waterwheel was a breast paddle. The only work it would perform was grinding. All else was done by hand, the sifting being by hand sieve, and there would be no fanners for blowing out the husks, this being done at the shelling hill.

In the relevant charters of which there were several, was included Glentig mill in the parish of Colmonell, also the property of the Stewarts shortly after 1668. The estate was acquired by the Whiteford's and was held by them for several generations. In 1948 it was the property of the Kennedys of Dunure.

A FINAL CHAPTER[78]

CROSBIE MILL

Crosbie or Corsbie Mill was in the barony of that name and was situated on one of the two burns which join below Monktonhill farm. The largest is the Rumbling Burn which rises near Knockindale and running towards the west past Burnbrae, Townend and High Wexford, it joins the other burn a short distance below the bridge at Monktonhill. The second burn rises near the village of Symington, and also runs to the west past Low Wexford and Hobsland and joins the Rumbling Burn. This burn had a dam about a quarter of a mile up and a lade conducted the water down to the farm for the purpose of driving a threshing mill and may have been used at an earlier date for driving a corn mill.

At the north east corner of the farmstead of Monktonhill were two buildings, the larger of which would appear to be the mill and the other the kiln for drying the corn. The waterwheel had been removed and the space in which it ran was the bed of the burn with a small dam in the tailrace. Its purpose may have been to keep the burn from scouring the foundations of the walls. The burn then continues on its course for a mile and, along with the water of the Rumbling Burn, discharges into the firth a quarter of a mile north of the Pow Burn.

Crosbie Mill is mention in a charter confirmed by Robert II. The King at Dundonald, December 4, 1371, confirmed a grant to Ade de Fulerton, knight, and his spouse Marjory of two merks sterling annually from the mill of Corbie. David Fullarton of Corsbie *in implement of a contract of marriage pact between James Fullarton, his son, on the one part, and John Fullarton of Dreghorn, Jean Mure Lady Dreghorn, his mother, and Agnes Fullarton, her daughter, on the other part for resigning the whole lands of Fullarton, Corsbie etc., together with the mills of Corsbie and Fullarton as also the advocation and patronage of the Kirk of Corsbie in His Majesty's hands in favour and for new infiftment to the said James Fullarton his son - dated September 22, 1593.* The family of Fullarton had held the estate of Crosbie from the time of Robert II, and resided in the old house of Crosbie from about 1500 to 1745 when a new house was built which was again called Fullarton. It was sold to the Duke of Portland in the year 1805 and later possessed by the town of Troon.

BARASSIE MILL

Barassie Mill was situated at the station of that name close to the bridge that carries the railway - the first to be run in Scotland, the Duke of Portland's mineral line from Troon to Kilmarnock, a distance of about nine miles. The mill house was so close to the railway that by putting our your hand from the window you could nearly touch the waggons passing. When the railway was opened the waggons were much smaller but they were always being increased in size and coming closer to the old building. The building was later removed.

The driving power for the mill was obtained from two burns that met in the retaining dam, which was near to the mill. One had its source near to Parkthorn, and, running to the west past Hillhouse, Laigh Hillhouse, and Barassie farms, entered the mill dam where there was a large fireclay pipe. The other burn has its origin near the reservoir, and passing Collenan and Struthers, joins the other burn in the mill dam. The land had been much disturbed making the lade and the dam difficult to trace.

The mill appears to have been working as late as 1835. It was in a corn-growing district but had one great drawback for a country corn mill. It was too close to the sea, so that all of the corn for grinding came from one side. About 130 years ago Irish corn was being imported at Troon, and there seems no doubt that Barassie Mill, being near the railway, got a share of the grinding. The Irish was inferior to Ayrshire corn, but when milled here it was dried with anthracite coal which gave the meal a better taste and colour than the peat-dried Irish. The mill was in the parish of Dundonald.

SCULLOCH MILL

Sculloch Mill was situated near Loans on the Ayr to Irvine road. The burn, which was the driving power of the mill, rises above Clevance and runs towards the west, passes the farm of Crossburn, thence under the Irvine road and continues down through the flat country for about a mile. It then joins the Darley burn which discharges its water into the North bay near the Mill Rock, Barassie. This burn, before reaching the Darley, was of low volume for driving a corn mill. However, Armstrong's map of Ayrshire (1775) shows that there were two lochs to the east of the mill at that time, a small one and one much larger; and the burn ran through them both. They may have been flooded hollows for collecting and retaining the water for the mill when required, and used only in the winter time being dried off in the summer for grazing or hay making.

In all probability the mill buildings became part of the farmstead of Crossburn. After the mill was closed the water wheel was used for driving a threshing mill - the place where it ran could be seen with the tailrace. According to Johnston's map of 1828 the farm steading of Crossburn was situated about a quarter of a mile to the south of the road crossing at Loans on the boundary of the two parishes of Dundonald and Monkton.

No return has been found of the miller who occupied this mill. In 1851 Robert Guthrie was farmer in Crossburn; in 1868 there was a Robert Guthrie, farmer in Loansparks, Struthers, and Barassie Moor.

There was another mill named Fullarton on the old barony of that name in or near the town of Irvine. The name Fullarton would suggest that it was erected at an early date as it is mentioned in some of the old charters, and being the barony mill was considered important. The old Castle or House of Fullarton was built near the estuary of the River Irvine and not far from a large tract of low, marshy lands which up to recently were overflowed with the waters of the river and the tides. It was here that the Baron granted a large tract of land to his fowler, and called it Fowler's farm.

APPENDIX - APPROXIMATE MAP REFERENCES

Fullarton Mill, Irvine ——————————————— 320382
Girvan Mill, Girvan ——————————————— 187978
Gittybeg Mill, near Dailly (Kittybeg Mill) ——————— 275008
Glenfoot Mill, Maidens ——————————————— 213078
Glentig Mill, Colmonell ——————————————— 145824
Glenwhask Mill, Barrhill ——————————————— 226834
Grange Mill, Culroy ——————————————— 319139
Green Mill, Cumnock ——————————————— 553204
Guiltree Mill, Kirkmichael ——————————————— 357095
Haugh Mill, near Mauchline ——————————————— 498253
Helenton Mill, Symington ——————————————— 395308
Heugh Mill, Symington ——————————————— 403305
Holehouse Mill, near Sorn ——————————————— 618270
Keir's Mill, near Straiton ——————————————— 395113
Ladyburn Mill, near Crosshill ——————————————— 206023
Littlemill, Rankinston ——————————————— 451152
Lochton Mill, Barhill ——————————————— 257802
Malt Mill, Newton on Ayr (Newton Mill) ——————— 338223
Mill Affleck,Ochiltree (Auchinleck Mill) ——————— 522210
Mill o' Ness, Sundrum ——————————————— 417213
Mill o' Sheil, near Barbieston ——————————————— 437178
Millmannoch, Coylton (Kilmanoch Mill) ——————— 432184
Milnholm Mill, near Annbank ——————————————— 387284
Milton Mill, near Straiton (Blairqhuan Mill) ——————— 374053
Monkton Mill, Monkton (Prestwick Mill) ——————— 344278
Monkland Mill, Heads of Ayr ——————————————— 295184
Monkswood Mill, near Minishant ——————————————— 273132
Muir Mill, near Muirkirk ——————————————— 652261
Nether Mill, Ayr (Old Town or Burgh Mill) ——————— 343215
Ochiltree Mill, Ochiltree ——————————————— 506218
Old Dailly Mill, Dailly (Camreggan Mill) ——————— 227993
Over Mill, Ayr ——————————————— 364217
Park Mill, Tarbolton ——————————————— 445272
Patna Mill, Patna ——————————————— 412113
Pinclanty Mill, near Barr ——————————————— 234913
Polnessan Waulk Mill, Polnessan ——————————————— 419117
Polquhairn Mill, Sinclairstone ——————————————— 478158
Powbank Mill, Prestwick ——————————————— 354268
Privick Mill, Annbank ——————————————— 407224
Purclewan Mill, near Dalrymple ——————————————— 380159
Scotlands Mill, Scotland's Bridge ——————————————— 422292
Sculloch Mill, near Troon ——————————————— 346291
Shalloch Mill, near Girvan ——————————————— 182955
Skeldon Nether Mill, near Hollybush ——————— 373137
Skerrington Mill, near Cumnock ——————————————— 573184
Sorn Mill, Sorn (Dalgean or Dalgain Mill) ——————— 560264
Tarbolton Mill, Tarbolton (Willie's Mill) ——————— 435277
Thomaston Mill, near Kirkoswald ——————————————— 225095
Trabboch Mill, Coylton ——————————————— 433211
Upper Mill, near Straiton ——————————————— 378053

Note. The map references are in the main approximate
and should be taken as indicative only.

References

1   The Ayrshire Post, January 11, 1944
2   Thirlage - an obligation to have grain ground in a particular mill
3   Multure - a proportion of corn retained by the miller as his due
4   The Ayrshire Post, Feb. 4, 1944
5   Munro, R. 1882 *Ancient Scottish Lake Dwellings*. Edinburgh.
6   The Ayrshire Post, Feb 11, 1944
7   The Ayrshire Post, February 25, 1944
8   The Ayrshire Post, March 1944
9   The Ayrshire Post, April 21, 1944
10   The Ayrshire Post, June 9, 1944
11   A supply of corn to be ground at one time
12   1844
13   None of the Mills are working now and in 1996 Millmannoch Mill was burnt down by vandals
14   Ayrshire Post, June 23, 1944
15   About 1790
16   The Ayrshire Post, July 7, 1944
17   The Ayrshire Post, July 21, 1944
18   Merk -rarely a coin but much used in reckoning
19   The Ayrshire Post, July 28, 1944
20   The Ayrshire Post, August 4, 1944
21   Blind Harry (Harry the Minstrel fl. 1470 - 92)   Author of narrative verses on The Acts and Deeds of Sir William Wallace.
22   The Ayrshire Post, August 11, 1944
23   The Ayrshire Post, September 1, 1944
24   Both Overmill and Barskimming Mills have ceased.
25   Approx 1844
26   The Ayrshire Post, September 22, 1944
27   Approx 1.25p
28   The Ayrshire Post, September 29, 1944
29   The Ayrshire Post, November 10, 1944
30   The Ayrshire Post, November 24, 1944
31   Approx 1814
32   Approx 1896
33   The Ayrshire Post, December 22, 1944
34   Tithes
35   The Ayrshire Post, January 19, 1945
36   Approx 1845
37   These mills were closed in 1959.
38   The Ayrshire Post, March 2, 1945
39   Also known locally as Queen Mary's Mortification. This was land endowed to the Burgh of Ayr for the maintenance of the reformed church and provision for poor relief and education.

40   The Ayrshire Post, March 23 1945
41   Handfull
42   The Ayrshire Post, May 4, 1945
43   The Ayrshire Post, August 23, 1946
44   The Ayrshire Post, August 23, 1946
45   The Ayrshire Post, August 30, 1946
46   Approx 6 bushels
47   The Ayrshire Post, September 6, 1946
48   The Ayrshire Post, September 30, 1946
49   The Ayrshire Post, September 27, 1946
50   The Ayrshire Post, November 1, 1946
51   The Ayrshire Post, December 27, 1946
52   Cloth Mill
53   The Ayrshire Post, January 3, 1947
54   Process of technical outlawry (by blasts of the horn by a messenger) whereby
      the goods of a debtor could be escheated to the crown and made available to
      creditors.
55   The Ayrshire Post, January 10, 1947
56   The Ayrshire Post, January 17, 1947
57   The Ayrshire Post, January 31, 1947
58   The Ayrshire Post, March 21, 1947
59   The Ayrshire Post, April 25, 1947
60   The Ayrshire Post, May 2, 1947
61   The Ayrshire Post, May 9, 1947
62   The Ayrshire Post, May 16, 1947
63   The Ayrshire Post, May 23, 1947
64   The Ayrshire Post, June 6, 1947
65   The Ayrshire Post, July 11, 1947
66   The Ayrshire Post, July 18, 1947
67   The Ayrshire Post, July 25, 1947
68   The Ayrshire Post, August 1, 1947
69   The Ayrshire Post, August 8, 1947
70   The Ayrshire Post, August 15, 1947
71   The Ayrshire Post, August 22, 1947
72   The Ayrshire Post, September 12, 1947
73   The Ayrshire Post September 19, 1947
74   The Ayrshire Post, September 26, 1947
75   The Ayrshire Post, January 2, 1948
76   The Ayrshire Post, January 16, 1948
77   The Ayrshire Post, January 30, 1948
78   The articles describing Crosbie Mill,Barassie Mill and Sculloch Mill did not
      apparently appear in the Ayrshire Post although proof copies are in
      the possession of the author's family.

PUBLICATIONS of the
AYRSHIRE ARCHAEOLOGICAL
& NATURAL HISTORY SOCIETY

available from
Ronald W Brash MA, Publications Distribution Manager
10 Robsland Avenue, Ayr, KA7 2RW

An Ayrshire Family 1526-1900 (Waterson)	£1.50
Ayrshire Honestones (Tucker)	£1.50
Ayrshire Mining Enterprises 1600-1840 (Whatley)	£1.50
Digging Up Old Ayr (Lindsay)	£1.00
George Lokert of Ayr (Broadie)	£1.25
A Scottish Renaissance Household (MacKenzie)	£3.00
The Shipping Trade of Ayrshire 1689 -1791 (Graham)	£3.60
Plant Life in Ayrshire (Kirkwood & Foulds)	£4.20
The Barony of Alloway 1324-1754 (Hendry)	£3.60
Robert Adam in Ayrshire (Sanderson)	£3.60
The Cumnock Pottery (Quail)	£5.00
Tolls and Tacksmen (McClure)	£3.60
Smuggling and the Ayrshire Economic Boom (Cullen)	£4.00
The Port of Ayr 1727-1780 (Graham)	£4.20
John Smith of Dalry. Part 1 - Geology (ed. Reid)	£6.00
John Smith of Dalry. Part 2 - Archaeology & Natural History (ed. Reid)	£7.20
Mauchline Memories of Robert Burns (ed. Strawhorn) (reprint)	£3.50
The Antiquities of Ayrshire (Grose, ed. Strawhorn) (reprint)	£4.20
Cessnock. An Ayrshire Estate in the Age of Improvement (Mair)	£4.50
Robert Reid Cunninghame of Seabank House (Graham)	£3.60
Historic Ayr: A Guide for Visitors	£2.00
A Community Rent Asunder (Mair)	£3.50
The Rise and Fall of Mining Communities in Central Ayrshire (Wark)	£3.00
Armstrong's Maps of Ayrshire (1775: reprint: 6 sheets)	£12.00